Coventry Pool and Garden House Plans

Coventry Pool and Garden House Plans

Including summerhouses
from England

MANOR HOUSE
PUBLISHING CO. INC.

Feasterville, Pennsylvania

MANOR HOUSE
PUBLISHING CO. INC.

Cover Photo Credit
Main photo: Steve Edmonds, courtesy of Pool & Spa Living Magazine;
Insets left to right: Robert and Laura Ryan; Tony D. Townley;
Manor House Publishing Co., Inc.; Amdega, Ltd.

Printed in the United States of America

Publisher's Cataloging-in-Publication
(Provided by Quality Books, Inc.)

Coventry pool & garden house plans : plus English
  summerhouses. -- 3rd ed.
    p. cm.
    Coventry pool and garden house plans
    "63 pool & garden houses. Detailed floor plans.
Architectural renderings."
    ISBN 0-9645844-7-6

    1. Garden structures--Designs and plans.
    2. Architecture, Domestic--Designs and plans. 3. Vacation
homes--Designs and plans.   I. Title: Coventry pool and
garden house plans.

    NA8450.C68 2003   728'.9'0222
                                 QBI03-200660

Warning and Disclaimer
The illustrations and floor plans in this catalog are approximate. Buyers should refer to the architectural plans they order for specific dimensions.
The approximate length and width dimensions noted with each plan include overhangs and porches. Illustrated features, such as landscaping, planters and
walkways, are not on the plans and are included in the illustrations to show you how a finished pool or garden house looks in a proper setting.

Table of Contents

Introduction

The Spirit in the Garden

*Y*ou placed it there, in your heart, years ago. In your vision it distinguishes the extraordinary from the ordinary. It creates new boundaries. It is brave and dares you to live in as dignified a manner as humanly possible. It is also a statement of achievement. And it is more practical than most can imagine. Perhaps now is the time to awaken the spirit you envisioned and fulfill the promise in your heart.

A New Standard for the American Dream

*W*elcome to Coventry Country, a world of luxurious pool and garden living. Here you will discover how to create an outdoor environment that is in complete harmony with your desired lifestyle.

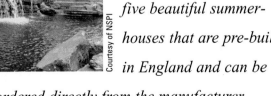

Courtesy of NSPI

On the following pages we have gathered many magnificent pool and garden houses that are exceptional in design and detail. Our architects and designers have redefined the word "cabana," or pool house, in dozens of extraordinary examples of American architecture. We have also created many delightful garden houses befitting the outdoor setting you have envisioned. Also, included for your viewing pleasure are five beautiful summer-houses that are pre-built in England and can be ordered directly from the manufacturer.

Each Coventry plan depicted in this book can be ordered on page 126. Peruse to your heart's content. Envision your dream. Then, select the perfect plan that will add new life to your home.

How to Select a Pool or
Garden House for Your Property

*I*n many ways it will be easier to select a pool or garden house than to select a new home. When choosing a place to live you must con-sider location, lot size, in some instances the school district and proximity to work, shopping and worship. Then, using one of the many home plan books available, you must select home style, size, floor plan, as well as pay atten-tion to dozens of other important details.

Here your focus is much easier. With location and the home of your dreams already fixed, everything is nearly perfect. You have exactly what you have always wanted, except...

...A Pool or Garden House Would Make Your Dream Complete

Perhaps you already have a swimming pool or are planning to have one built. If you are among the millions of happy pool owners, you already realize the great advantage of owning a pool house, or a "cabana," as it is sometimes called.

Most pool house owners would agree that having a pool without the pool house is like having a car without gas. A pool house adds so much to the lifestyle of leisure living and saves so many headaches and unnecessary trips to the main house. Especially at party time.

Traditionally, pool houses were places for guests to change. But today their functionality goes

beyond the change room. They sometimes have a bathroom and an outside or inside shower. Many times, they have both. Some pool houses have entertaining areas or covered areas to keep out the sun. There are pool houses in every size and description. Some have storage areas for towels and pool supplies. Others can be modified to include pool equip-ment. And, if you choose, they can have all the items listed above and also become perfect winter storage areas for furniture, floats and unrelated outdoor items.

Even if you are building your first swimming pool, it will not take you long to realize how convenient, beautiful and absolutely special pool houses really are.

A Garden House Can Add So Much Value to Your Lifestyle

You do not have to be a garden tinkerer to own a garden house. In some ways, a garden house can be nothing more than a fantasy that you allow yourself to own. In other ways, it is as necessary as a pool house, a garage or even a kitchen sink.

A garden house can be exactly what you want it to be. Families use garden houses for different reasons. One use is as a storage shed for lawn and garden equipment. But, a garden house can be far more functional. Some families use them for tea houses; for potting sheds; for combined pool supplies and general storage areas. Sometimes they simply add sparkle and color to the garden landscape. Yes, garden houses and their functions vary by owner and property need. And, like pool houses, they sometimes match or even contrast the styling of the main house.

In this catalog many pool houses can easily be converted to garden houses to help you achieve almost any design effect.

Live With the Plans before You Build

If you are ready to build, this catalog is probably the most important find you have made to date. Other than having a group of great architects and garden designers at your fingertips, there may be no finer collection of pool or garden houses that can spark important ideas and designs that fit your vision.

Even if you are not quite ready to start building a pool or garden house today, you may want to order a set of plans of a pool or garden house that interests you. Some families order one set of plans and live with that set to be sure that they have selected the perfect pool or garden house that suits their particular lifestyle. It could be the most inexpensive decision one makes when planning to build.

Whichever idea fits your particular needs, *Coventry Pool and Garden House Plans* is ready to help you proceed.

Summerhouses are the Perfect Getaways from Everyday Life.

Amdega Limited

Your dream is almost a reality: the English garden you have been planning is nearly finished. You researched every detail and the results are perfect. Except, you need a summerhouse to complete the landscape. You want to keep things authentic. Amdega LTD summerhouses has the answer.

Based in England, but with consultants around the world, Amdega LTD has been constructing quality summerhouses since 1874. Each is made with solid, rot-resistant Canadian western red cedar, which can be stained or painted in one of Amdega's botanical colors. The interior walls are lined with oak veneered plywood and the roofs are tiled with cedar shingles.

The windows have traditional leaded glass and the floors are made of solid wood. Although all can be placed on concrete bases or paved terraces, certain models can be mounted on turntables that revolve to follow the sun. Electricity can be run if you want to turn your summerhouse into an office or a studio, or if you just want to light and heat your little getaway.

You need to contact Amdega LTD directly for information. Call 1-800-449-7348 to reach a design consultant who will work with you to devise the best plan for your summerhouse. You may also write for information: Amdega/Machin, 16 Ostend Avenue, Westport, CT 06880.

A Pool House

You will wonder how you ever got along without it!

A wise man once said: "Give to yourself the pleasures that you seek before it is too late to enjoy them." A swimming pool with a complementing pool house is one of those exquisite pleasures. Just ask the person who has both. A pool house makes a pool more rewarding. It is that simple.

Appearance Alone Impresses

One of the prime reasons to own a swimming pool, although pool owners will not always admit it, is aesthetics. The yard, the garden, or that special enclave where you place your swimming pool helps create an environment most Americans covet. Now, add to this picture a structure that frames the setting and adds its own beauty to the landscape. The results are incredibly stunning.

Steve Edmonds

Functionality

A pool house not only looks good, but it also is a fantastic place to entertain if you have children, if you plan to have alfresco parties or if elegant outdoor dining is in your future. A pool house is one of those havens that will make your day, almost every day.

Adding a pool house means more than simply keeping grassy feet off the Oriental carpet. It is about having the ability to entertain elegantly outside in the afternoon or on a balmy evening under the stars. It is about convenience, just as indoor plumbing and central heating (once considered luxuries) have replaced the outhouse and the open fire.

Think about not having to run inside the house to greet your guests, one by one, as they arrive. Think about the advantages when you or one of your guests want to grab a quick drink or use the bathroom. Even better, imagine yourself enjoying your own party, not wondering if someone is inside your house while you are outside talking with guests.

Off-Season Benefits

Ever wonder where to put chemicals when they are not in use? Ever ponder where to send the crowd of children when a quick rain shower breaks out? Ever think about reclaiming your garage or basement in the off-season by storing lawn furniture, toys and floats elsewhere? Your new pool house will be the perfect place for all of that and more. A pool house is no longer a place that is reserved for the Hollywood glamour set; it is surprisingly affordable and extremely useful.

The Seaside

The Fairview

Courtesy of NSPI

Build Now or Add Later

Some pool builders are already offering a pool house as an option. They are small custom builders who understand what their customers are really looking for. These builders take pride in constructing a few special pools and designing them in a first class manner. But, this type of builder is still uncommon, and most homeowners who want a pool house will have to rely on the old-fashioned way: building the pool first and then complementing it with a pool house.

Buy a Set of Plans

Another approach is to spend some time looking at a pool house catalog to understand the array of choices that are available to you. In addition to changing rooms and bathrooms, you will discover innovative plans that include handy serving windows, entertainment areas and lots of poolside storage space.

On the following pages are 50 different designs, ranging from a pool house that looks like a conservatory to one that resembles a southwestern villa. If you find a pool house design that intrigues you, it is easy to order a set of building plans so that you can have them available to show your builder.

Even if you are planning to hire a professional, it is a good idea to be aware of the many and varied choices so that you can work more effectively with your builder or architect.

For That Distinctive Touch

If you are planning to have a new swimming pool built some time soon, or if you want to enhance the pleasure and extend the entertaining capabilities of the one that you already have, consider adding a pool house—that respite you have always wanted. 🌿

Storybook Pool House

"It all began with a desire to do something extraordinary," says Bambi Offield of Keller, Texas. "My husband and I purchased a set of pool house plans we had seen advertised in a magazine. We were looking for a plan that would allow us to do a lot of outdoor entertaining, so it had to have a changing room for guests, a full bath, complete with shower, and a good size

The Offields modified the floor plans to the Hacienda (see page 50) to create their dream pool house.

kitchen so that no one would have to go into the main house for anything. I'd say convenience and the idea of entertaining outdoors were the driving forces. The other big benefit of our pool house is that it certainly keeps our home from getting messed up."

Besides the convenience aspect, the Offields' pool house has added a dramatic backdrop to their already beautiful swimming pool. "People are always stopping by to ask about it," Bambi continues. "It's a real attention-getter, especially for families who own a pool and like to keep wet feet outdoors—where they belong."

The Offields purchased their house plan from *Coventry Pool and Garden House Plans*, then added

their own special creativity, which most plan purchasers do. "The model we chose, the Hacienda, already had a southwest flair, so we made some modifications to the front elevation and made it our version of the 'Alamo,'" Bambi says, smiling.

On the back elevation, the Offields again used their design abilities to produce yet another look. "Since the pool house can be seen from the road, we dressed up the rear elevation to look like an Italian grotto." There are stairs that descend to the castle-like wine cellar built under the pool house itself. "It's a party place and it is themed to be a lot of fun. The plan we bought gave us the canvas to do our thing, and we loved every minute of it."

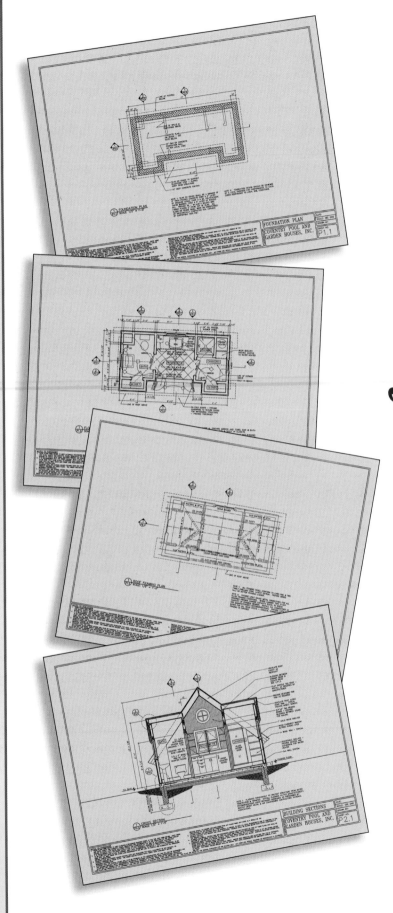

What Our Pool and Garden House Plans Include

*T*he illustrations and floor plans shown in this catalog are approximate. Buyers should refer to the architectural plans they order for specific dimensions. The approximate length and width dimensions noted with each plan include overhangs and porches. Illustrated features, such as landscaping, planters and walkways, are not on the plans and are included in the illustrations to show you how a finished pool or garden house looks in a proper setting.

Exterior Elevations

These drawings show the front, rear and sides of the buildings and give specific information on the exterior finishing materials shown in the catalog. Special attention is given to distinctive construction details of each pool and garden house.

Foundation Plan

Shows the complete foundation layout. Most are shown as slab construction, others with crawl space construction. Professional builders can readily change the foundation to meet local codes and to accommodate soil and other conditions on your property.

Floor Plans

Show the precise layout of your pool or garden house. Rooms, doors and windows are dimensioned, and keys are given for cross-sections located elsewhere in your plans. Recommended positions of plumbing fixtures and wall outlets are shown.

Cross Sections

These show sections or cut-aways of each aspect of the buildings, from foundation to roofline. Since the sections show exactly how materials relate to each other, the cross sections are especially important to your builder.

Roof Details

Show the slope, pitch and location of dormers, gables and other roof elements on these details, elevation plans or sections.

Interior Elevations

Show the design and placement of cabinets, built-ins and other special interior features, as needed.

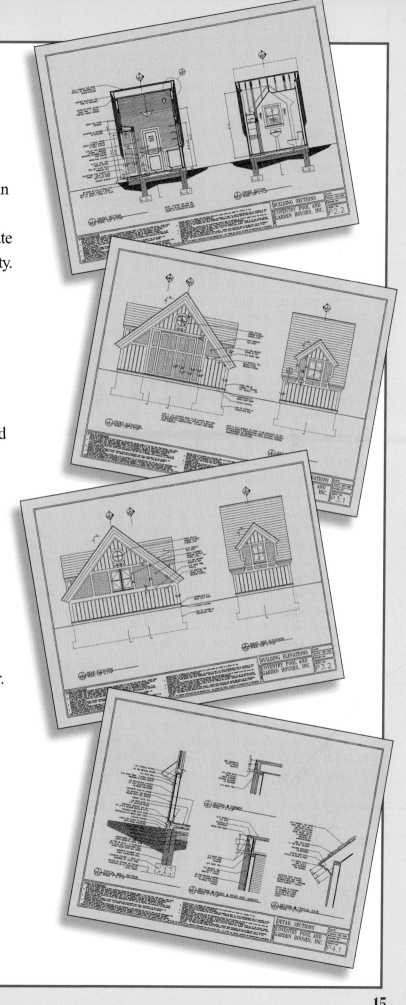

Alegría

*T*he cantilevered trellis over the serving window distinguishes the Alegría from other designs. The serving window is bound to get plenty of use since the kitchenette is equipped with sink, cabinets and an under-the-counter refrigerator. In addition to the changing room/bathroom, note the nice storage closet behind the sliding doors.

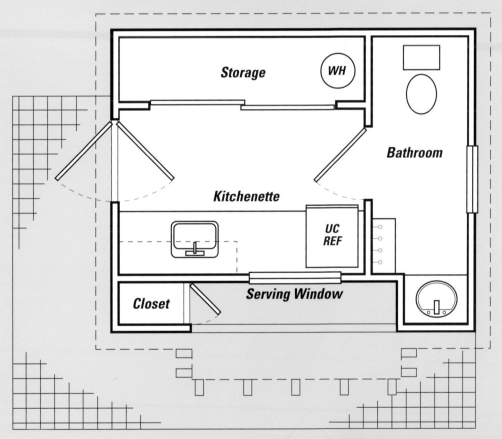

Alegría Plan # 216

Bathroom	Kitchenette	Closet	Storage	Serving Window	Footprint (approximate)	Gross Area* (approximate)
✓	✓	✓	✓	✓	12' x 10'	14' x 14'

*Suggested minimum area to build this plan to accommodate door openings, roof overhangs, exterior walls, treatments and easy access.

Ashton

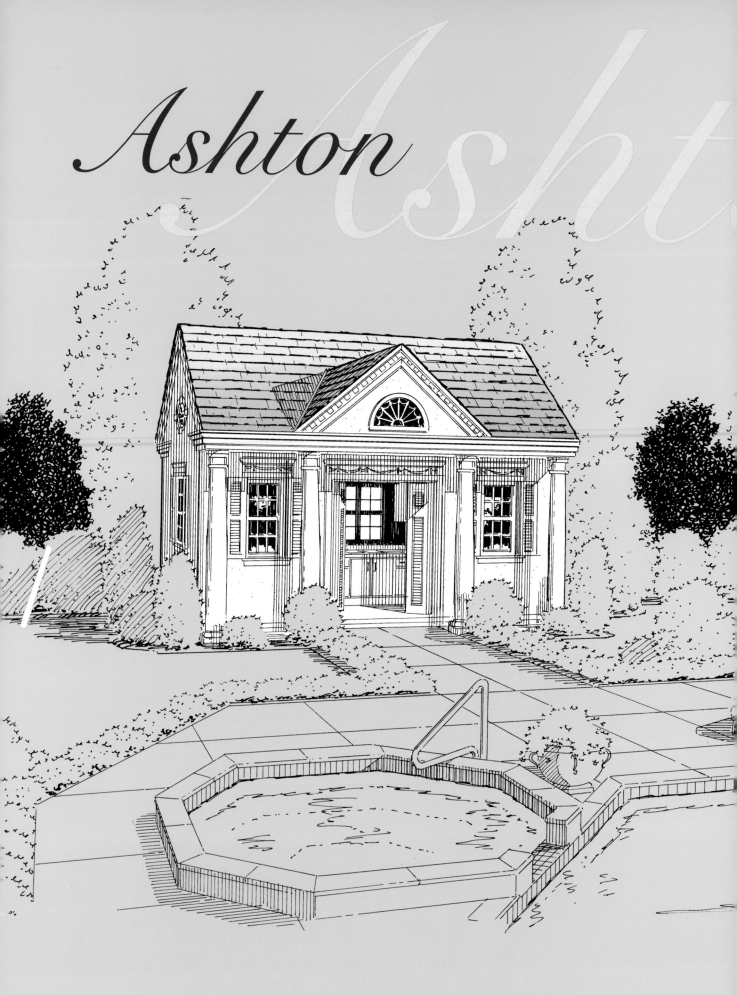

*T*he stately columns and dentil molding make this charming Colonial a welcome addition to any property. It boasts a complete bathroom, including the privacy of an indoor shower, and a handy kitchenette that beckons when you are ready for refreshments. The storage area is large enough to hold your pool equipment, power mower and the family's bicycles.

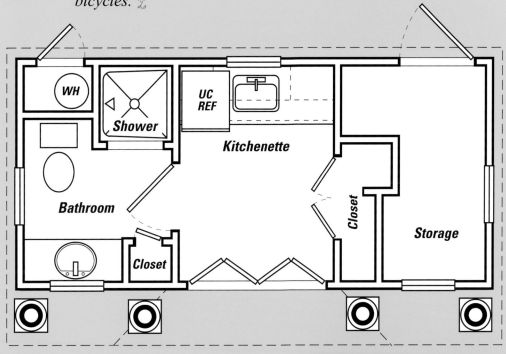

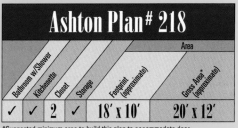

Ashton Plan # 218

Bathroom w/Shower	Kitchenette	Closet	Storage	Footprint (approximate)	Gross Area* (approximate)
✓	✓	2	✓	18' x 10'	20' x 12'

*Suggested minimum area to build this plan to accommodate door openings, roof overhangs, exterior walls, treatments and easy access.

Barrington

The Barrington brings the Federal style to life with its glass quoins and classical pediment over the double-door entrance. There is plenty of storage space, with a wide storage area in back and a closet on each side. You will be able to entertain the crowd from work easily since the Barrington has a changing room/bathroom on one side and a changing room with shower on the other side. Plus, there is an outdoor shower, a great extra amenity.

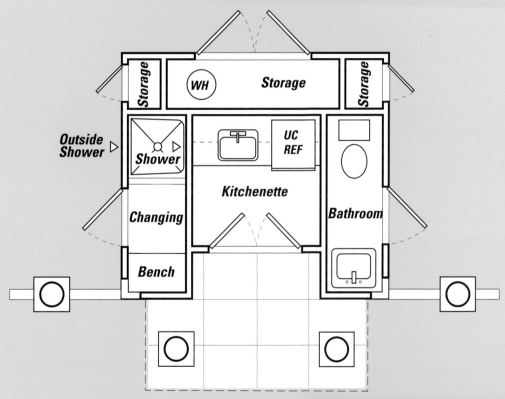

Barrington Plan# 220

Changing Area w/Shower	Bathroom	Outside Shower	Kitchenette	Storage	Footprint (approximate)	Area	Gross Area* (approximate)
✓	✓	✓	✓	3	13' x 15'		18' x 18'

*Suggested minimum area to build this plan to accommodate door openings, roof overhangs, exterior walls, treatments and easy access.

Breezewood

ou can almost feel the gentle breeze stirring the

air around the open design of the Breezewood. There

is space for a changing room and a shower in one area,

and a bathroom and two storage closets with outdoor access

in another. Add the barbecue, the stone chimney and the covered

porch, and the result is pure New England charm.

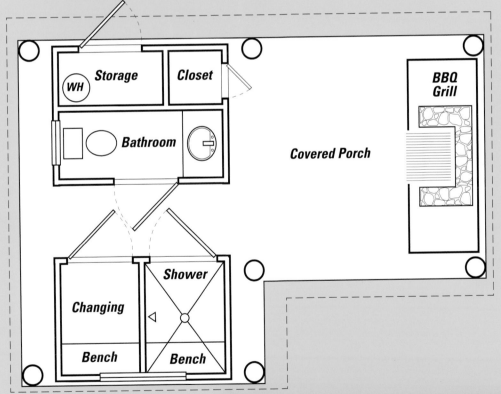

Bromley

*N*o matter where you live, you will feel as if you and your guests are away on vacation when you own this delightful English Cottage pool house. It has an extra changing room in addition to the bathroom, and each room has its own clothes closet. Add the welcoming feeling of the wide entry and the airy kitchenette, and you can see why the Bromley is such a favorite.

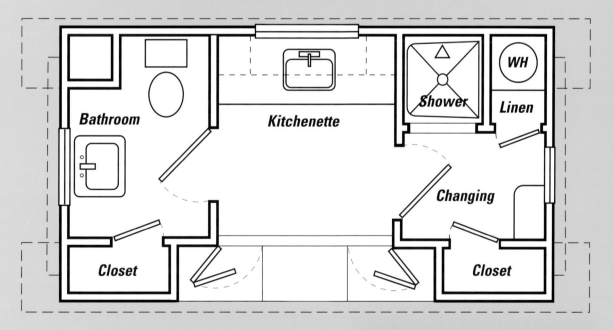

Bromley Plan# 224

Changing Area w/Shower	Bathroom	Kitchenette	Closet	Footprint (approximate)	Gross Area* (approximate)
✓	✓	✓	3	17' x 9'	20' x 12'

*Suggested minimum area to build this plan to accommodate door openings, roof overhangs, exterior walls, treatments and easy access.

lise's

*H*ere is a pool house your friends and neighbors will never stop talking about. The unique Art Deco design features an oversize round window with companion circles on the front door. The large kitchen area can be accessed from the front or from the convenient sliding doors that open onto the covered porch. It is easy to picture yourself toweling off, getting a cool drink and relaxing in the shade of these imaginative surroundings.

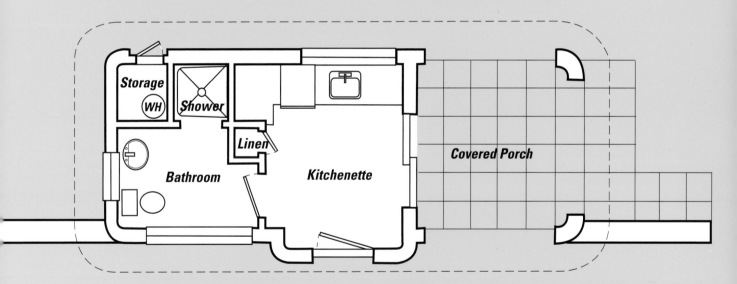

Captain's Paradise Plan# 226

Bathroom w/Shower	Kitchenette	Closet	Storage	Covered Porch	Footprint (approximate)	Gross Area* (approximate)
					Area	
✓	✓	✓	✓	✓	24.5' x 12'	42' x 16'

*Suggested minimum area to build this plan to accommodate door
openings, roof overhangs, exterior walls, treatments and easy access.

t's

O n the outside, this exciting showpiece has the same Art
Deco approach as Captain's Paradise. However, the
kitchenette is in clear view of the spectacular round window.
First-time visitors will have little difficulty finding your house. Just tell
them to look for the only pool house in the neighborhood with
a decorative parapet and flagpole.

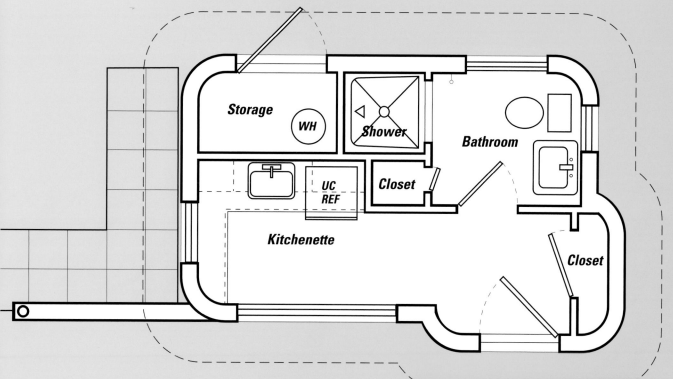

		Captain's Retreat Plan # 228				
					Area	
Bathroom w/Shower	Kitchenette	Closet	Storage	Footprint (approximate)		Gross Area* (approximate)
✓	✓	2	✓	25' x 12'		26' x 15'

*Suggested minimum area to build this plan to accommodate door
openings, roof overhangs, exterior walls, treatments and easy access.

Carlisle

The Carlisle is reserved for families that really want to make dreams come true. The eye-catching design is unique, and the wraparound wings help you accommodate a crowd. You will especially appreciate the availability of extras, such as space for a refrigerator, laundry facilities and hidden storage above the entry area.

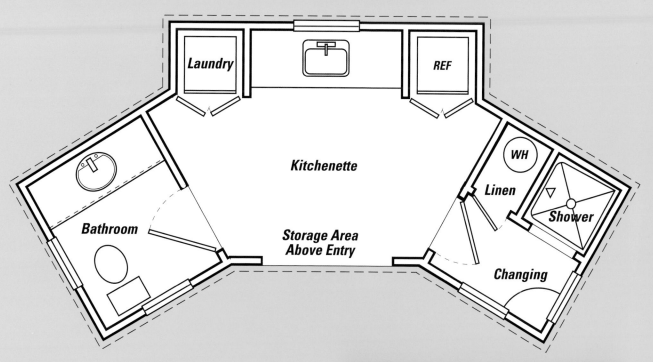

Laundry

REF

WH

Kitchenette

Linen

Shower

Bathroom

Storage Area
Above Entry

Changing

Carlisle Plan# 230

Changing Area w/Shower	Bathroom	Kitchenette	Laundry Room	Closet	Storage	Footprint (approximate in')	Area Gross Area* (approximate in')
✓	✓	✓	✓	✓	✓	24' x 12.5'	27' x 14'

*Suggested minimum area to build this plan to accommodate door openings, roof overhangs, exterior walls, treatments and easy access.

Chandler

*H*ere is a Victorian design that will add beauty and interest to any scene. Note how the impressive detailing combines with the large overhang to give you the perfect exterior look. And, when it is your turn to be the waiter or waitress, you will enjoy "setting them up" at the poolside serving windows that are part of the kitchenette.

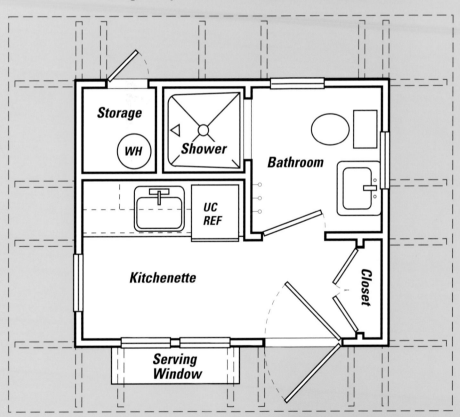

Chandler Plan # 232

| | | | | | | Area | |
Bathroom w/Shower	Kitchenette	Closet	Storage	Serving Window	Footprint (approximate)	Gross Area* (approximate)	
✓	✓	✓	✓	2	12.5' x 10'	18' x 16'	

*Suggested minimum area to build this plan to accommodate door openings, roof overhangs, exterior walls, treatments and easy access.

Concord

The pool area will never look the same after you marry a sunny afternoon and this perfect Federal-style design. Guests can freshen up in complete privacy and then join your family for a Sunday cookout. The kids will be able to pass cool drinks through the convenient serving window, while you attend to the hot dogs and hamburgers on the outdoor barbecue.

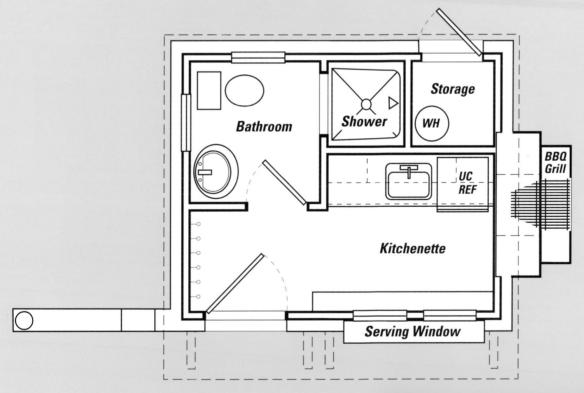

Bathroom w/Shower	Kitchenette	Barbecue Grill	Storage	Serving Window	Footprint (approximate)	Area Gross Area* (approximate)
✓	✓	✓	✓	2	22' x 11'	24' x 14'

*Suggested minimum area to build this plan to accommodate door openings, roof overhangs, exterior walls, treatments and easy access.

Cumberland

*F*or a family that favors outdoor entertaining and has a spacious property adjoining the pool, the Cumberland is almost irresistible. When you are hosting your best customers, a cousin's club or your daughter's classmates, you will make great use of the uncommonly large covered area, the outdoor barbecue and the kitchenette's sliding doors.

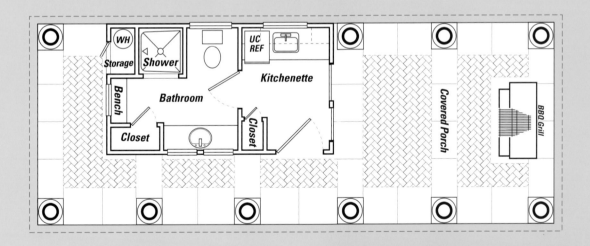

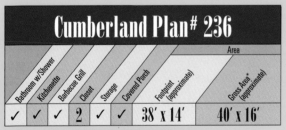

Cumberland Plan # 236

Bathroom w/Shower	Kitchenette	Barbecue Grill	Closet	Storage	Covered Porch	Footprint (approximate)	Area — Gross Area* (approximate)
✓	✓	✓	2	✓	✓	38' x 14'	40' x 16'

*Suggested minimum area to build this plan to accommodate door openings, roof overhangs, exterior walls, treatments and easy access.

Cypress

*T*he sliding door entryway is the first thing you notice about the Cypress. The spacious kitchenette, the bathroom with a shower and the two storage areas with outside doors make this pool house absolutely perfect for everyone who is thinking about poolside entertaining.

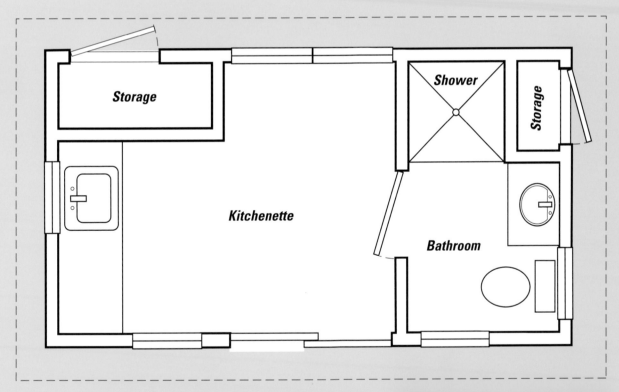

Cypress Plan # 238

| | | | | Area | |
Bathroom w/Shower	Kitchenette	Storage	Footprint (approximate)	Gross Area* (approximate)	
✓	✓	2	16.6' x 9'	20' x 13'	

*Suggested minimum area to build this plan to accommodate door openings, roof overhangs, exterior walls, treatments and easy access.

Dorchester

hester

*W*hen we see a classical Southern Colonial design like the Dorchester, it makes us happy that this popular style is built all over the country and not just in the South. Functional as well, the Dorchester has a shower in the center and changing rooms on each side. It would be appropriate for the signs on the changing rooms to read "Scarlett" and "Rhett."

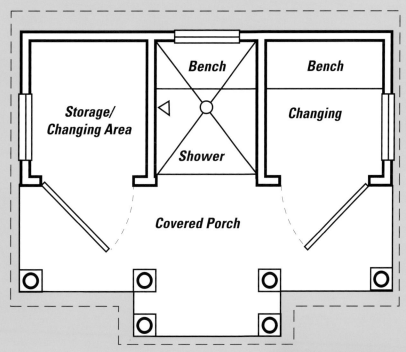

Dorchester Plan# 240

Changing Area	Shower	Storage/Changing Area	Covered Porch	Footprint (approximate)	Area Gross Area* (approximate)
✓	✓	✓	✓	11.6' x 9.6'	13' x 10'

*Suggested minimum area to build this plan to accommodate door openings, roof overhangs, exterior walls, treatments and easy access.

El Sol

It is common for the Spanish style to have stucco walls, a clay tile roof and extended beams, but they have never been combined with the flair of El Sol. That is especially true when you add dramatic sloping roofs and decorative parapets. El Sol has just about every feature one could want in a pool house, all set off by a large covered walkway.

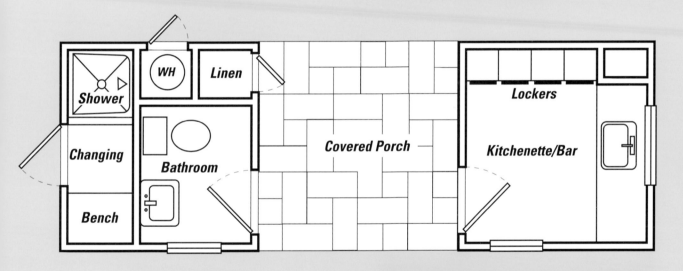

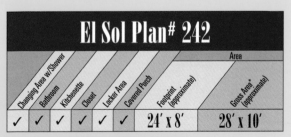

	Changing Area w/Shower	Bathroom	Kitchenette	Closet	Locker Area	Covered Porch	Footprint (approximate)	Gross Area* (approximate)
	✓	✓	✓	✓	✓	✓	24' x 8'	28' x 10'

*Suggested minimum area to build this plan to accommodate door openings, roof overhangs, exterior walls, treatments and easy access.

Emerson

con

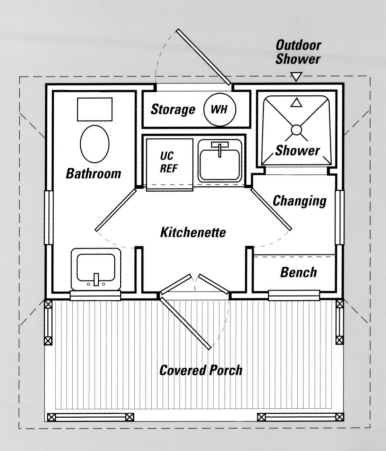

Outdoor Shower

Storage   WH

Bathroom

UC REF

Shower

Changing

Kitchenette

Bench

Covered Porch

The gingerbread appointments of this Victorian are so striking that everyone describes it the same way: a jewel-box. Your family will like the handy kitchenette, and there will never be a waiting line when you have the convenience of an inside shower and an outside shower. And, when you have had enough of the pool for a while, just get a magazine and enjoy the shade of the large covered porch.

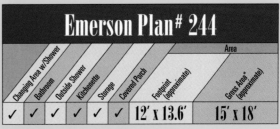

Emerson Plan # 244

Changing Area w/Shower	Bathroom	Outside Shower	Kitchenette	Storage	Covered Porch	Footprint (approximate)	Gross Area* (approximate)
							Area
✓	✓	✓	✓	✓	✓	12' x 13.6'	15' x 18'

*Suggested minimum area to build this plan to accommodate door openings, roof overhangs, exterior walls, treatments and easy access.

Fairview

*T*he Fairview is a great example of what happens when you achieve that delicate balance between functionality and simplicity of design. A large storage area with an outside entrance, a kitchenette with a sink and an under-the-counter refrigerator, and a spacious bathroom with a shower explain why the Fairview qualifies for the class vote of "most likely to succeed."

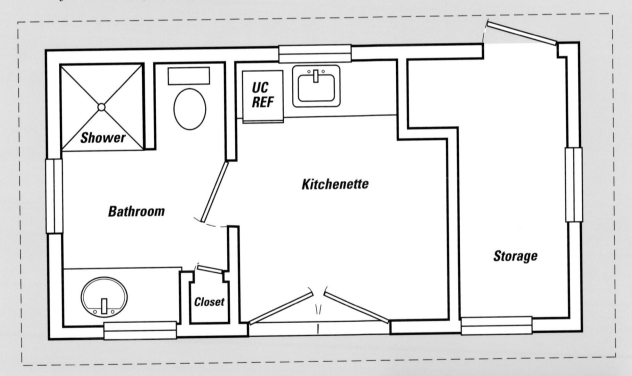

Fairview Plan # 246

Bathroom w/Shower	Kitchenette	Closet	Storage	Footprint (approximate)	Area Gross Area* (approximate)
✓	✓	✓	✓	19.6' x 10'	24' x 17'

*Suggested minimum area to build this plan to accommodate door openings, roof overhangs, exterior walls, treatments and easy access.

Glenville

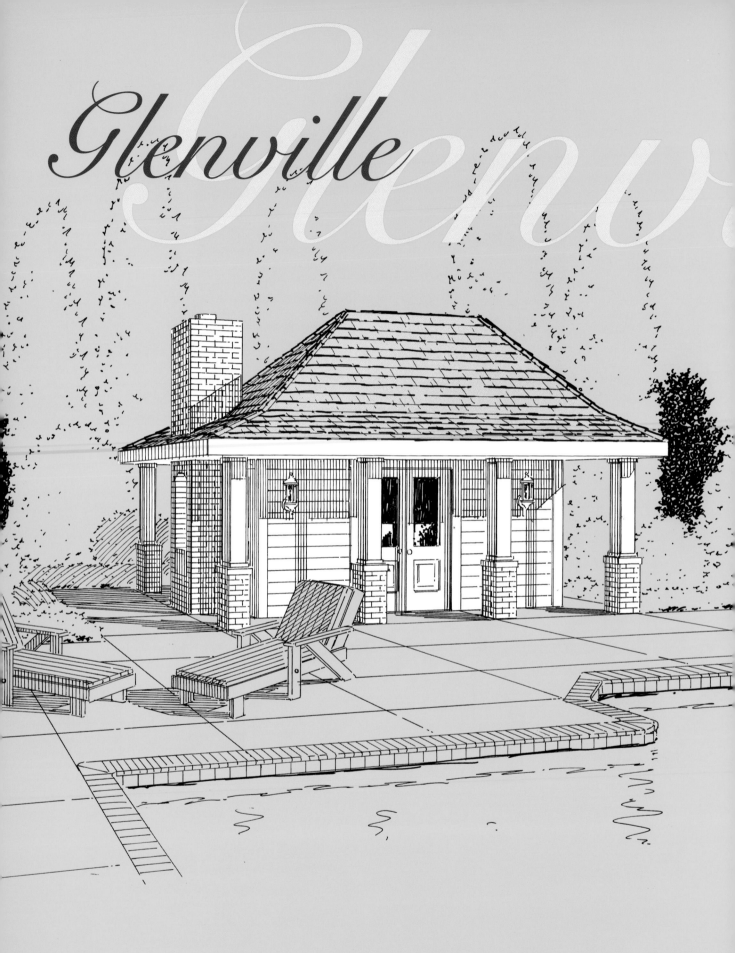

*T*he brick and wooden posts and the outdoor gas grill
are the first things you notice on the Glenville. Inside, you will
find a bathroom and shower, as well as a changing room. When
you have the Glenville, you will never be short of storage space. It has a long,
indoor storage room and convenient shelving on both sides of the grill. 🦢

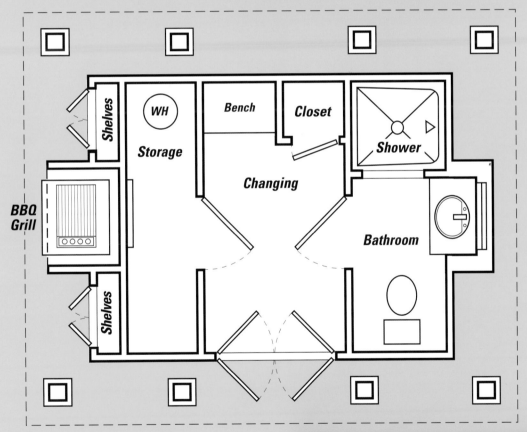

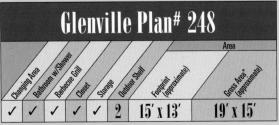

	Changing Area	Bathroom w/Shower	Barbecue Grill	Closet	Storage	Outdoor Shelf	Footprint (approximate)	Gross Area* (approximate)
	✓	✓	✓	✓	✓	2	15' x 13'	19' x 15'

*Suggested minimum area to build this plan to accommodate door
openings, roof overhangs, exterior walls, treatments and easy access.

Hacienda

*T*he Joneses will be in tears when they find out you are building the Hacienda. It has a changing room on one side and a bathroom with a shower on the other side. But the game will be over when they find out about the three skylights, the four separate storage closets, the custom door and the custom windows surrounded by ceramic tiles. Neither standard pool houses nor the Joneses will ever be the same again. ❦

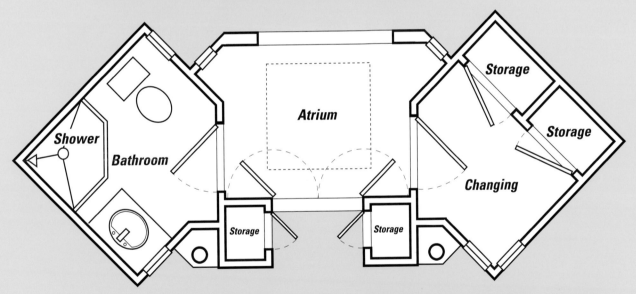

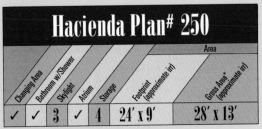

Hacienda Plan# 250

Changing Area	Bathroom w/Shower	Skylight	Atrium	Storage	Footprint (approximate in')	Gross Area* (approximate in')
✓	✓	3	✓	4	24' x 9'	28' x 13'

*Suggested minimum area to build this plan to accommodate door openings, roof overhangs, exterior walls, treatments and easy access.

Hamilton

*Y*ou will never want for comfort with the Hamilton. It has a built-in window seat in the bayed front and an outdoor wraparound bench. Your family and guests will make good use of the serving bar by taking advantage of the pass-through window and customized serving sill. And, while you are appreciating special design features, be sure to notice the outdoor shower that is discreetly tucked around back.

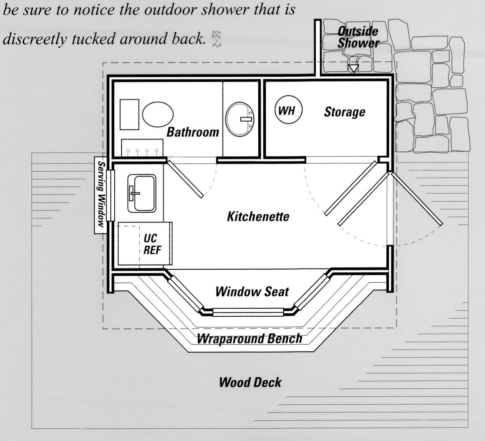

	Bathroom	Outside Shower	Kitchenette	Storage	Serving Window	Window Seat	Outdoor Wraparound Bench	Wood Deck	Footprint (approximate)	Gross Area* (approximate)
										Area
	✓	✓	✓	✓	✓	✓	✓	✓	12' x 10'	17' x 13'

Hamilton Plan# 252

*Suggested minimum area to build this plan to accommodate door openings, roof overhangs, exterior walls, treatments and easy access.

Hancock

*P*icture this: five friends are over for a swim party. The first one is taking a shower; the second is getting a snack in the kitchenette; the third has just changed and is hanging his clothes in the closet; the fourth is getting a float from the storage area; and the fifth is using the bathroom to change—and they are all in separate places in this great pool house. Now add decorator doors, an interesting metal-clad dormer and the charm of a New England Colonial, and the rest is pure magic.

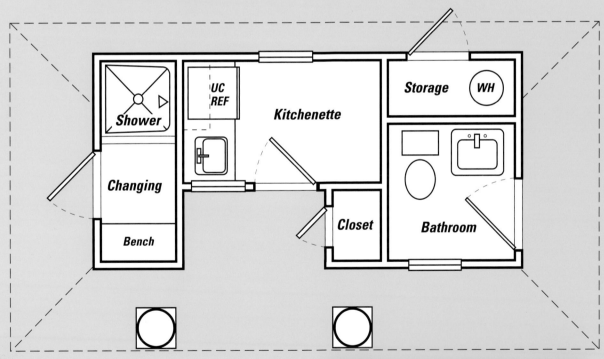

Hancock Plan # 254

	Changing Area w/Shower	Bathroom	Kitchenette	Closet	Storage	Footprint (approximate)	Area Gross Area* (approximate)
	✓	✓	✓	✓	✓	18' x 12'	24' x 15'

*Suggested minimum area to build this plan to accommodate door openings, roof overhangs, exterior walls, treatments and easy access.

Kenwood

ood

There is always something special about a Victorian design that is graced with a traditional cupola and weather vane. In the case of the Kenwood, the beauty is on the inside as well, with an airy kitchenette and handy serving windows. Just as you would want, there are a bathroom, a changing room with shower and a closet to use either for linens or as a clothing locker.

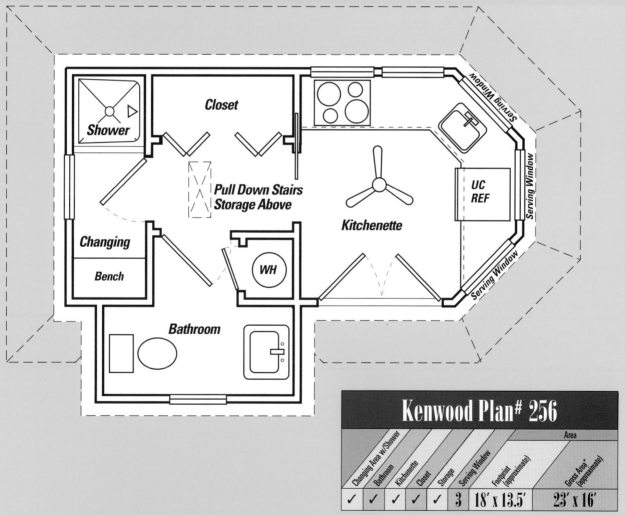

Kenwood Plan# 256

Changing Area w/ Shower	Bathroom	Kitchenette	Closet	Storage	Serving Window	Footprint (approximate)	Area
							Gross Area* (approximate)
✓	✓	✓	✓	✓	3	18' x 13.5'	23' x 16'

*Suggested minimum area to build this plan to accommodate door openings, roof overhangs, exterior walls, treatments and easy access.

57

La Bonita

*I*t is easy to picture yourself hosting your favorite friends when you have an outdoor barbecue, a covered porch and a spacious kitchenette with a convenient serving window. Also, in addition to the roomy bathroom, there is a changing room with a shower. If the Mission Style works well on your property, you will love the elegant design and appointments of La Bonita.

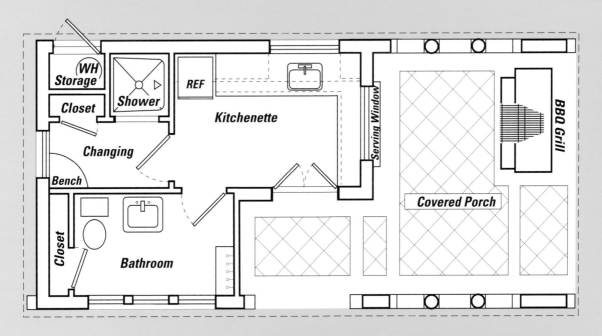

La Bonita Plan# 258

Changing Area w/Shower	Bathroom	Kitchenette	Barbecue Grill	Closet	Storage	Serving Window	Covered Porch	Footprint (approximate)	Gross Area* (approximate)
								Area	
✓	✓	✓	✓	2	✓	✓	✓	28' x 14'	31' x 18'

*Suggested minimum area to build this plan to accommodate door openings, roof overhangs, exterior walls, treatments and easy access.

Laguna

The glass block windows, metal roof and curved lines make the back of the Laguna so exciting you almost wish you could build it on an oversized Lazy Susan. But, no matter, since everything about the Laguna is stylish, including the outdoor shower and shower umbrella hidden behind the extended plant wall. Be sure to notice the two outdoor storage closets. One is handy for those using the shower, while the other is well out of the way.

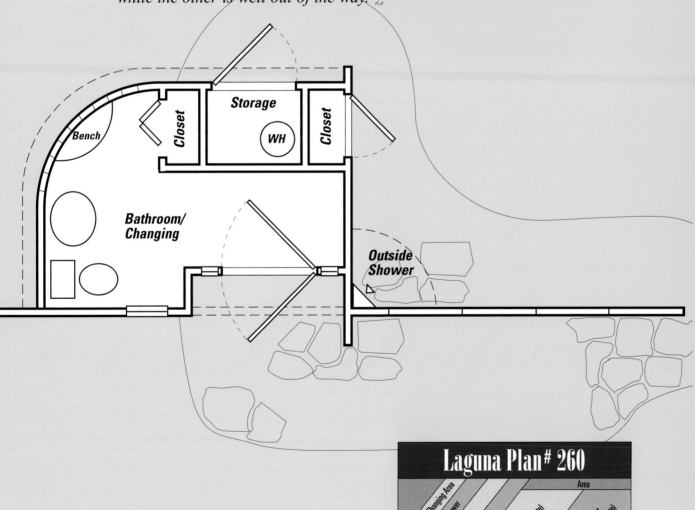

Laguna Plan# 260					
Bathroom/Changing Area	Outside Shower	Closet	Storage	Footprint (approximate)	Area Gross Area* (approximate)
✓	✓	2	✓	24' x 10.5'	27' x 12'

*Suggested minimum area to build this plan to accommodate door openings, roof overhangs, exterior walls, treatments and easy access.

Lansford

otice how the Lansford uses space to create privacy and separate areas. On one side there is a changing room/bathroom, while on the other side there is a large storage area. In the middle, in its own world, is the snack bar with a sink and under-the-counter refrigerator. Small wonder that the Lansford is the ideal choice for those who prefer a Dutch Colonial look.

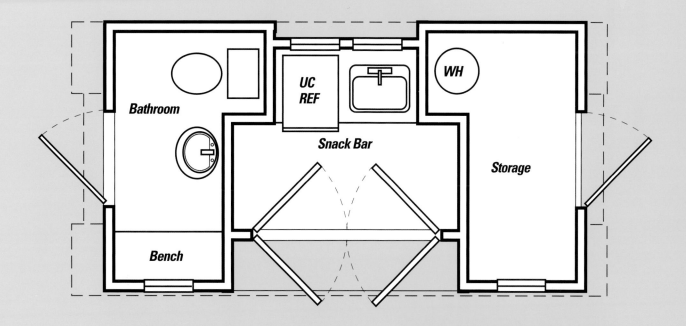

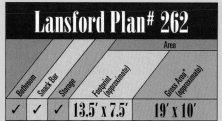

Lansford Plan# 262					
				Area	
Bathroom	Snack Bar	Storage	Footprint (approximate)	Gross Area* (approximate)	
✓	✓	✓	13.5' x 7.5'	19' x 10'	

*Suggested minimum area to build this plan to accommodate door openings, roof overhangs, exterior walls, treatments and easy access.

Marquesa

he freestanding canopy roof and the pavilions make the Marquesa precious in more ways than one. When it is time to take a breather from the sun and water, the children can have a playroom all to themselves without bringing dripping bathing suits and muddy feet into your house. And they will come on the double when they see the barbecue treats you have prepared for them. 🦎

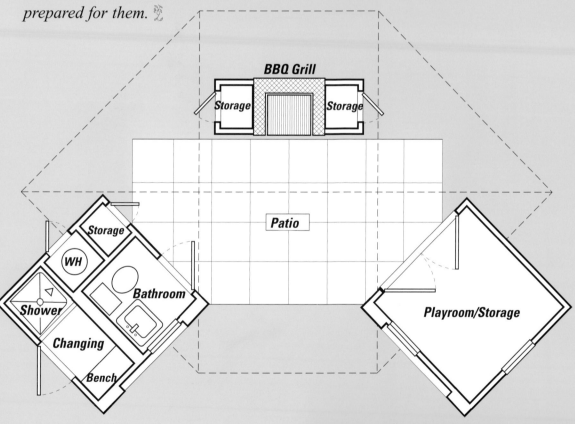

BBQ Grill

Storage | Storage

Patio

Storage

WH

Shower

Bathroom

Changing

Bench

Playroom/Storage

Marquesa Plan # 264

Changing Area w/Shower	Bathroom	Playroom/Storage	Barbecue Grill	Storage	Patio	Footprint (approximate)	Gross Area* (approximate)
							Area
✓	✓	✓	✓	3	✓	31' x 17'	33' x 22'

*Suggested minimum area to build this plan to accommodate door
openings, roof overhangs, exterior walls, treatments and easy access.

Milford

*T*he Milford is decorated with an angled bay window
on one side and designer-touch columns on the other.
The privacy section has an open changing area, a clothes
closet and a bathroom with shower. And, if you and your family spend
a lot of time outdoors, you will love the large kitchen with double doors
that leads to the covered patio.

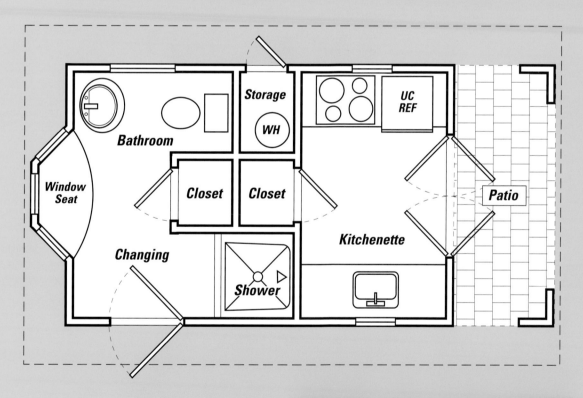

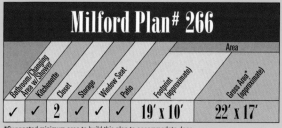

Milford Plan # 266

Bathroom/Changing Area w/ Shower	Kitchenette	Closet	Storage	Window Seat	Patio	Area	
						Footprint (approximate)	Gross Area* (approximate)
✓	✓	2	✓	✓	✓	19' x 10'	22' x 17'

*Suggested minimum area to build this plan to accommodate door
openings, roof overhangs, exterior walls, treatments and easy access.

Montegra

egra

A spacious bathroom that doubles as a place to change is just what you would want in a new pool house. But, that is only the beginning. Additional features are an extra changing room, a second shower and a storage area that is out of the way, yet easily accessible. The wing walls add a special feeling of privacy to this Spanish Baroque beauty.

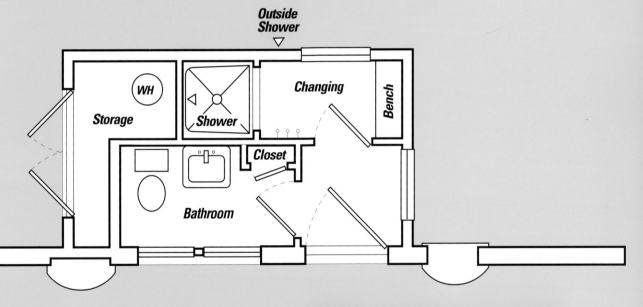

Outside Shower

Storage

WH

Shower

Changing

Bench

Closet

Bathroom

Montegra Plan# 268

Changing Area w/Shower	Bathroom	Outdoor Shower	Closet	Storage	Footprint (approximate)	Area Gross Area² (approximate)
✓	✓	✓	✓	✓	31.5' x 9.6'	33' x 12'

*Suggested minimum area to build this plan to accommodate door openings, roof overhangs, exterior walls, treatments and easy access.

Montpelier

elier

*B*eauty, grace, delicacy and refinement are terms that characterize most Victorian designs, and all of these terms fit the Montpelier perfectly. Just one look at its decorative porch, in this case with a cathedral ceiling, tells the story. The Montpelier has two changing rooms and two storage closets—all with their own outdoor access doors—as well as an outdoor shower.

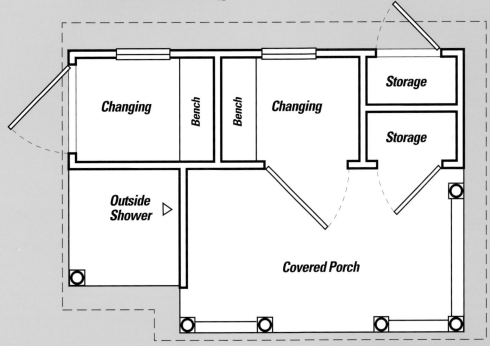

Montpelier Plan# 270

Changing Area	Outside Shower	Storage	Covered Porch	Footprint (approximate)	Area Gross Area* (approximate)
2	✓	2	✓	12' x 8.6'	15' x 13'

*Suggested minimum area to build this plan to accommodate door openings, roof overhangs, exterior walls, treatments and easy access.

Newfield

*D*uring the day, you will enjoy the flood of light from the glass-block clerestory and the skylights that have been set into the dramatic metal roof. In the evening, these same features provide a soft glow of charm and romance. And, when it comes to functionality, it is hard to top the convenience of two changing rooms and two outdoor showers that are shielded for privacy by stepped wing walls.

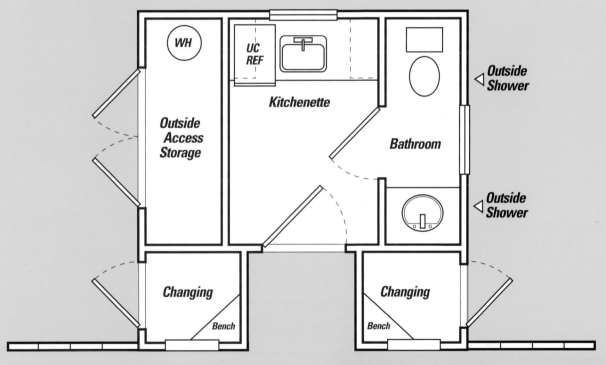

Newfield Plan # 272

Changing Area	Bathroom	Outside Shower	Kitchenette	Skylight	Storage	Footprint (approximate)	Gross Area* (approximate)
2	✓	2	✓	2	✓	21.5' x 12'	24' x 16'

*Suggested minimum area to build this plan to accommodate door openings, roof overhangs, exterior walls, treatments and easy access.

he Southern Colonial look is irresistible to many families, especially if it has the high columns of the Pendleton. It has three separate changing rooms when you include the bathroom—as most families do. Add the special touches, like a twelve-foot-high ceiling, above-the-door windows and an outdoor shower, and you can see why the Pendleton is so special.

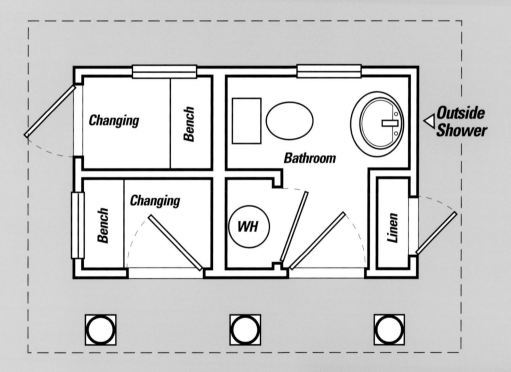

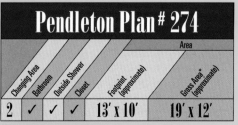

Pendleton Plan # 274

Changing Area	Bathroom	Outside Shower	Closet	Footprint (approximate)	Gross Area* (approximate)
					Area
2	✓	✓	✓	13' x 10'	19' x 12'

*Suggested minimum area to build this plan to accommodate door openings, roof overhangs, exterior walls, treatments and easy access.

Pennington

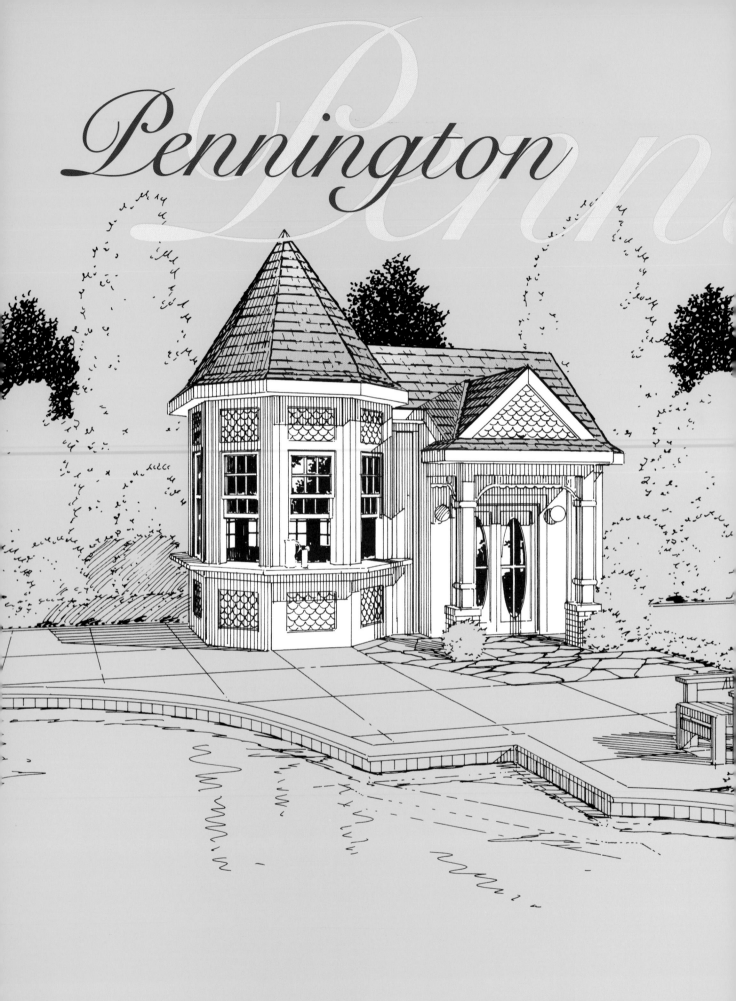

*Y*ou will find it hard to resist this Victorian's charming combination of octagonal design, turret roof and decorative scalloped shingles. With a sink, stove, under-the-counter refrigerator, roomy counter top and serving window, the kitchenette is sized for a family that really enjoys entertaining. You can just picture your guests taking advantage of the handy serving sill when they step up for their favorite drinks on a hot summer afternoon.

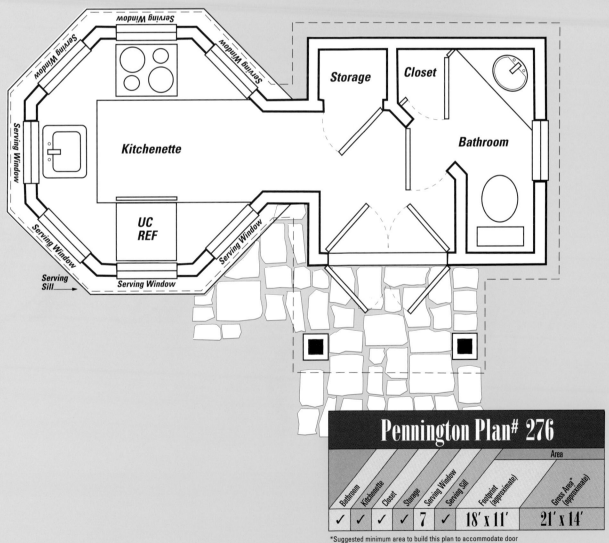

Serving Window

Serving Window

Serving Window

Serving Window

Storage

Closet

Serving Window

Bathroom

Kitchenette

UC REF

Serving Window

Serving Sill

Serving Window

							Area	
Bathroom	Kitchenette	Closet	Storage	Serving Window	Serving Sill	Footprint* (approximate)	Gross Area* (approximate)	
✓	✓	✓	✓	7	✓	18' x 11'	21' x 14'	

Pennington Plan# 276

*Suggested minimum area to build this plan to accommodate door openings, roof overhangs, exterior walls, treatments and easy access.

Piedmont

*T*he Piedmont has a changing room and a shower, as you might expect, but it is the third room that is a surprise. It can be a storage area—if that is your desire, a greenhouse—if you wish, or a great potting shed. You name it. And the potbelly stove will assure your complete comfort on those chilly spring or fall evenings.

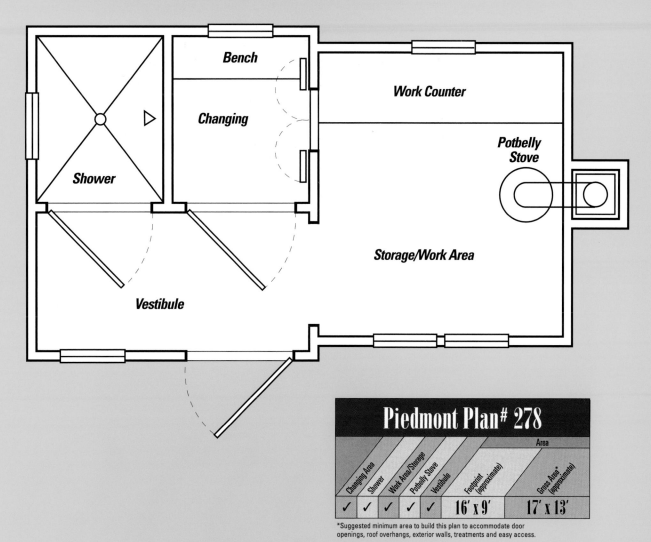

Piedmont Plan# 278

						Area	
Changing Area	Shower	Work Area/Storage	Potbelly Stove	Vestibule	Footprint (approximate)		Gross Area* (approximate)
✓	✓	✓	✓	✓	16' x 9'		17' x 13'

*Suggested minimum area to build this plan to accommodate door openings, roof overhangs, exterior walls, treatments and easy access.

Rockford

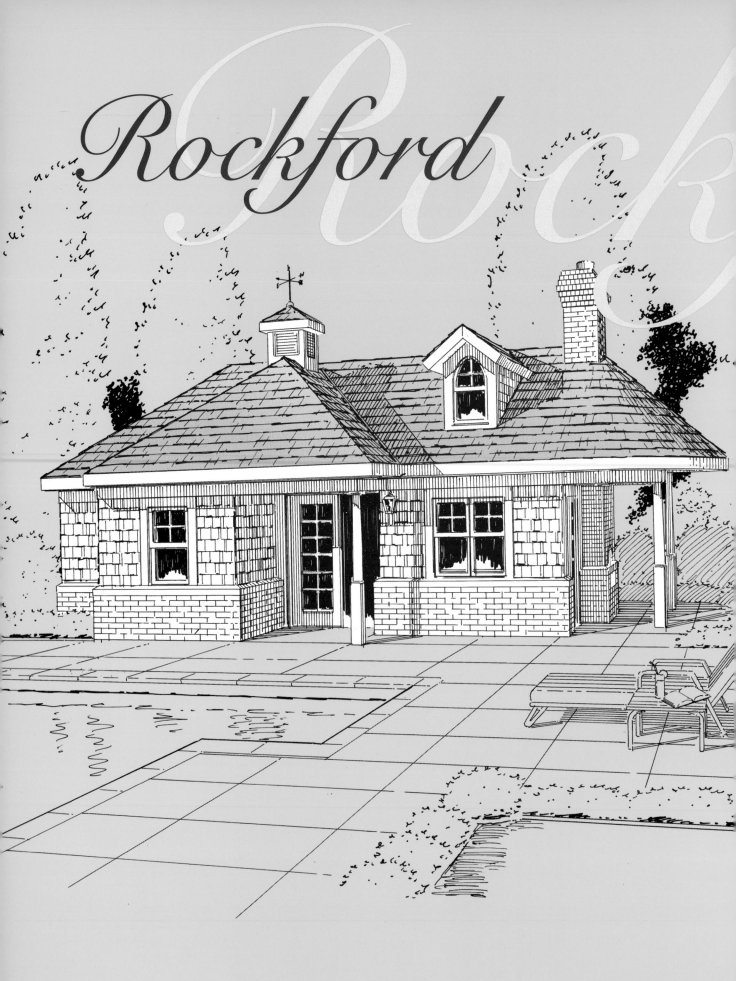

ord

*W*ith its rounded roof, decorative dormer and corbelled brick chimney, the Rockford may be just the answer if you have decided to go all out. In the changing area there is plenty of room for a large family, while the entertainment side has a kitchenette, a large playroom and an outdoor barbecue to cook up your family's favorite meal with all the trimmings.

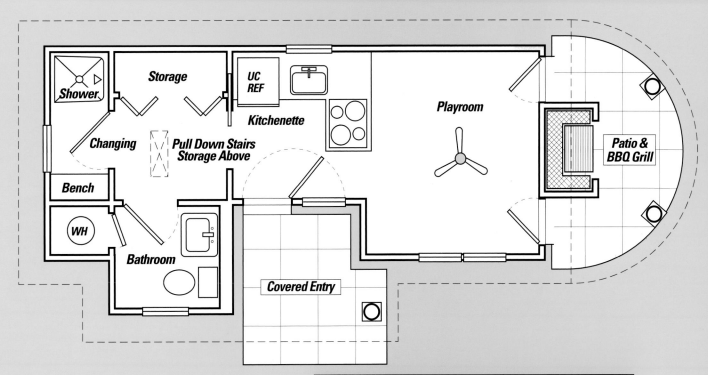

Rockford Plan# 280

Changing Area w/Shower	Bathroom	Playroom	Kitchenette	Storage	Barbecue Grill	Covered Entry	Patio	Footprint (approximate)	Area Gross Area* (approximate)
✓	✓	✓	✓	2	✓	✓	✓	29' x 13.6'	32' x 16'

*Suggested minimum area to build this plan to accommodate door openings, roof overhangs, exterior walls, treatments and easy access.

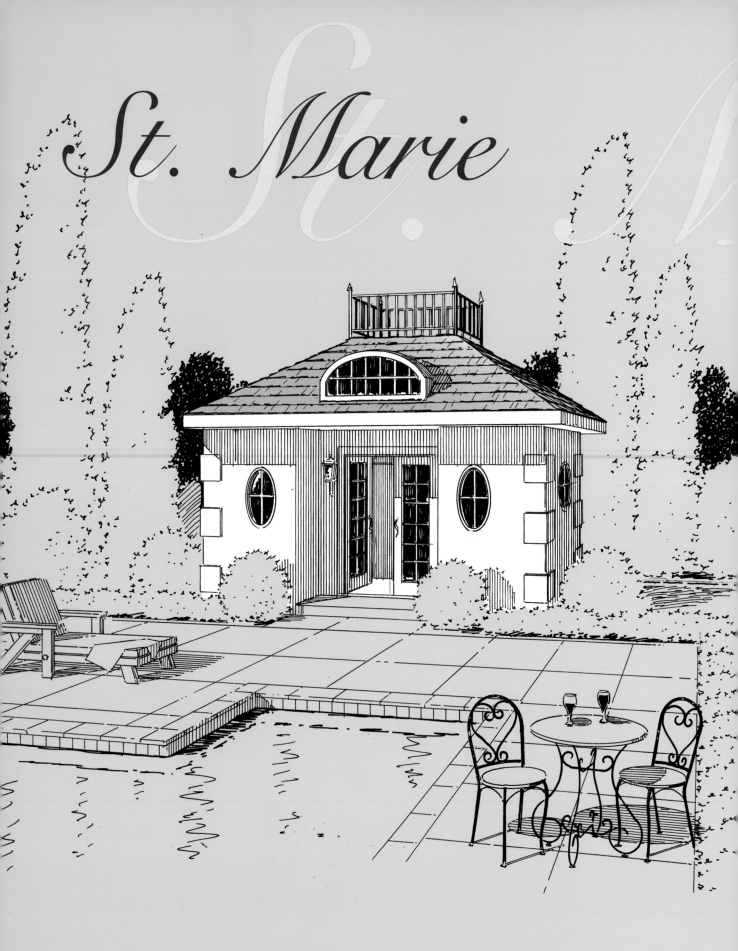

St. Marie

Marie

*T*he French design permeates the St. Marie from the French eyebrow window to the French doors and oval windows. The wrought-iron railing and decorative quoins continue the attractive theme. The St. Marie makes full use of its interior space, with pocket doors on both the bathroom and the changing room with shower.

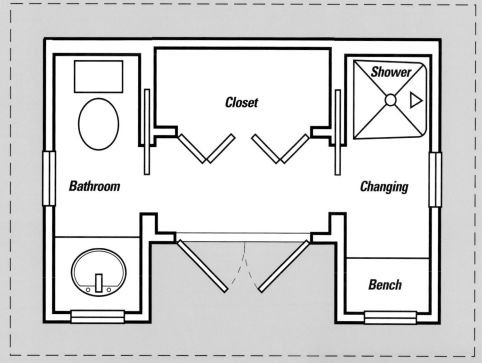

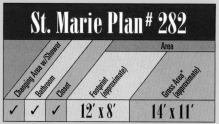

St. Marie Plan # 282

| | | | Area | |
Changing Area w/Shower	Bathroom	Closet	Footprint (approximate)	Gross Area* (approximate)
✓	✓	✓	12' x 8'	14' x 11'

*Suggested minimum area to build this plan to accommodate door openings, roof overhangs, exterior walls, treatments and easy access.

Seaside

*W*hen the louvered shutter is up, the oversized serving window in
the Seaside is so appealing that you almost wish it had a sign in red letters
that read "Refreshments." The spacious kitchenette has light streaming in from
three sides, including the one side with sliding glass doors. Note the changing room and
separate shower in back, and the outdoor storage closet that is large enough to hold
everything you may now have squeezed up against the back wall of your garage.

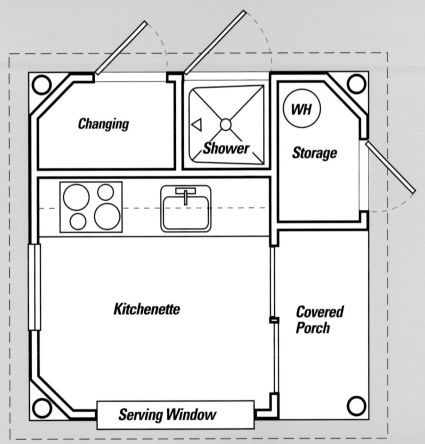

Seaside Plan# 284

							Area	
Changing Area	Shower	Kitchenette	Storage	Serving Window	Covered Porch	Footprint (approximate)		Gross Area* (approximate)
✓	✓	✓	✓	✓	✓	12' x 12'		16' x 16'

*Suggested minimum area to build this plan to accommodate door
openings, roof overhangs, exterior walls, treatments and easy access.

Shelby

*T*he Shelby is a fine example of the features that make a Victorian pool house design so popular. Note the distinctive tower as well as the decorative trim and columns. To store pool chemicals and equipment, you will want to use the double-door storage area on the side. It is nice to be able to have these things stored away from the high-traffic area of the kitchenette, the bathroom and the extra changing room and shower.

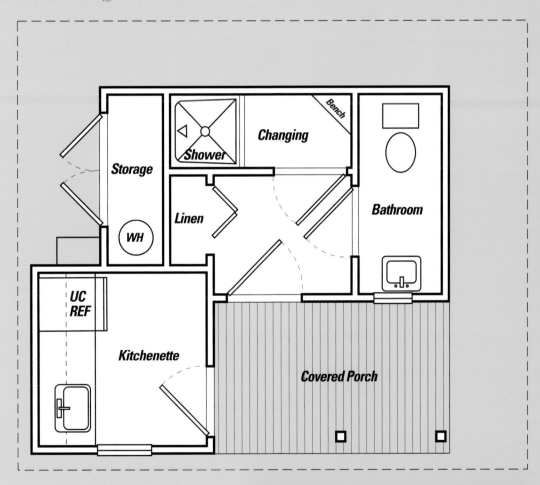

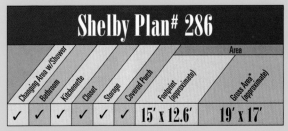

	Changing Area w/Shower	Bathroom	Kitchenette	Closet	Storage	Covered Porch	Footprint (approximate)	Area	
								Gross Area* (approximate)	
Shelby Plan# 286	✓	✓	✓	✓	✓	✓	15' x 12.6'	19' x 17'	

*Suggested minimum area to build this plan to accommodate door openings, roof overhangs, exterior walls, treatments and easy access.

Springdale

dale

*I*f you have not sold the air rights to your property, you will want to give the Springdale serious consideration. The changing room/ bathroom is in the back, while the kitchenette and serving windows are positioned for more frequent use. Do not be surprised if you need a family lottery to decide who gets to relax in the privacy of the beautiful balcony.

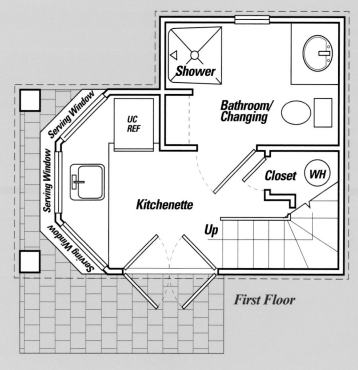

First Floor

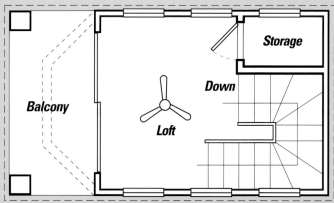

Second Floor

Springdale Plan# 288

First Floor	Bathroom/ Changing Area/Shower	Kitchenette	Closet	Serving Window	Staircase	Second Floor	Loft	Balcony	Storage	Footprint (approximate)	Gross Area* (approximate)
	✓	✓	✓	3	✓		✓	✓	✓	11' x 15'	16' x 17'

*Suggested minimum area to build this plan to accommodate door openings, roof overhangs, exterior walls, treatments and easy access.

Sundance

nce

*T*he sharp pitch of the seamed metal roof and the drama of custom windows announce this special design. Like many other Coventry designs, the Sundance is ideal for evening entertaining as well as daytime use. It is easy to picture the caterer taking advantage of the spacious kitchen to prepare cocktails and hors d'oeuvres. And note that the balcony is large enough to hold its own "conversation group," while others gather near the pool. 🦐

First Floor

Second Floor

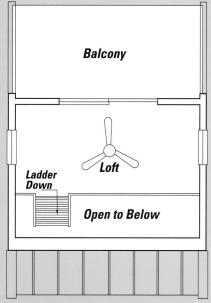

	First Floor	Bathroom w/Shower	Kitchen	Bar	Storage	Window Seat	Pull-down Ladder	Second Floor	Loft	Balcony	Footprint (approximate)	Gross Area* (approximate)
	✓	✓	✓	✓	✓	✓			✓	✓	12' x 17'	14' x 19'

Sundance Plan # 290

Area

*Suggested minimum area to build this plan to accommodate door openings, roof overhangs, exterior walls, treatments and easy access.

The Tower

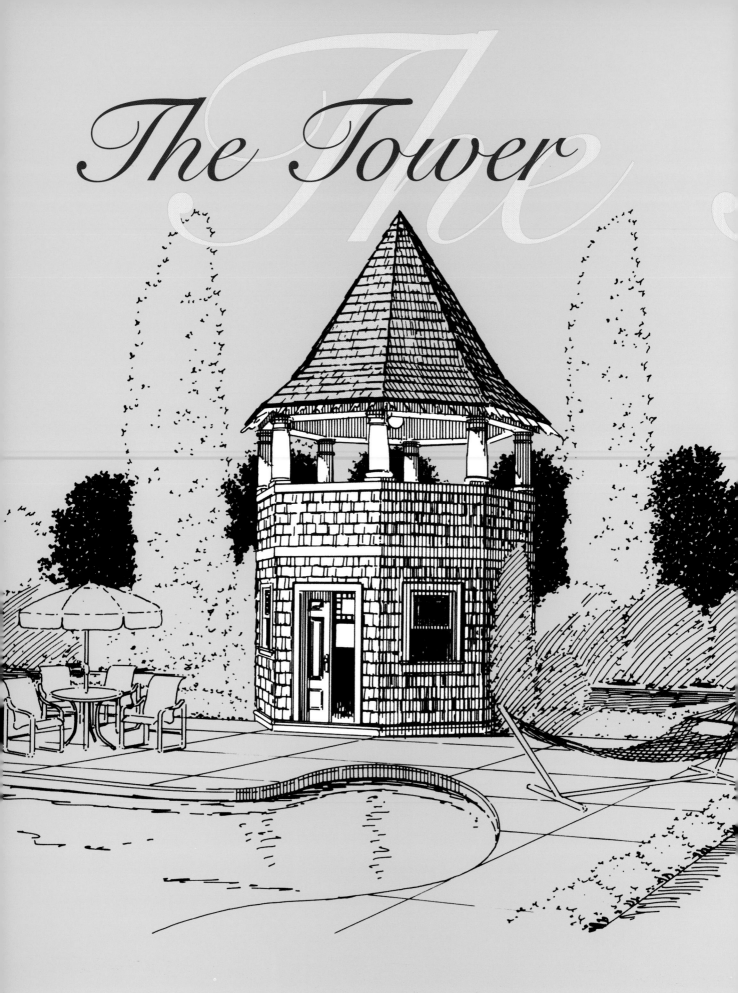

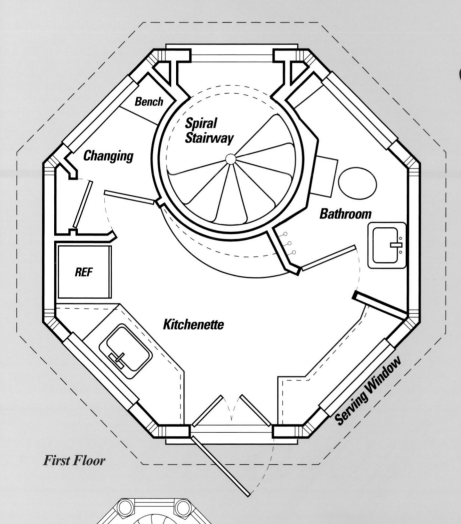

Bench

Spiral Stairway

Changing

Bathroom

REF

Kitchenette

Serving Window

First Floor

Spiral Stairway

Landing

Second Floor

*I*f you appreciate uniqueness, you will find the octagonal shape of The Tower a special treat. You enter the circular stairway at the rear of The Tower and climb to the landing to have shaded privacy or to watch the crowd having fun in the pool. Note that the kitchenette, with its handy serving window, is large enough to serve everyone without the help of a local caterer.

The Tower Plan # 292

| | | | | | | | | Area | |
First Floor	Changing Area	Bathroom	Kitchenette	Serving Window	Spiral Stairway	Second Floor	Landing	Footprint (approximate)	Gross Area* (approximate)
✓	✓	✓	✓	✓		✓		14.5' x 14.5'	18' x 19'

*Suggested minimum area to build this plan to accommodate door openings, roof overhangs, exterior walls, treatments and easy access.

Townsend

send

*T*t is a given that the Townsend goes with any Tudor
style home, but this particular design is so easy to live
with that it is compatible with many other styles as well.
There is a space for a changing room and an open shower on one
side and two closets with outdoor access on the other. Of course, the
larger storage area can easily be another changing room, depending
upon your family's needs. Either way the Townsend is a winner.

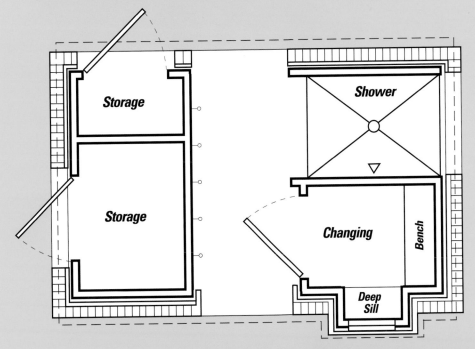

Townsend Plan # 294						
					Area	
Changing Area	Shower	Storage	Deep Sill	Footprint (approximate)	Gross Area* (approximate)	
✓	✓	2	✓	12.6' x 8'	17' x 13'	

*Suggested minimum area to build this plan to accommodate door
openings, roof overhangs, exterior walls, treatments and easy access.

Valencia

*T*he open trellis and patio of the Valencia give it that extra touch of class, especially when combined with the exposed rafters that extend on all four sides. It is nice to have a kitchen sink in any pool house, but the Valencia goes even further, with a bar and second kitchen sink. This way you can accommodate adults as well as children when the pool gets a lot of use on a holiday weekend.

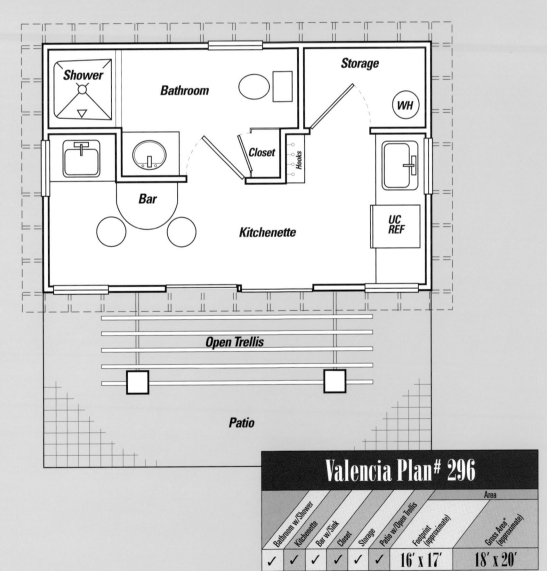

Valencia Plan# 296

Bathroom w/Shower	Kitchenette	Bar w/Sink	Closet	Storage	Patio w/Open Trellis	Area	
						Footprint (approximate)	Gross Area* (approximate)
✓	✓	✓	✓	✓	✓	16' x 17'	18' x 20'

*Suggested minimum area to build this plan to accommodate door openings, roof overhangs, exterior walls, treatments and easy access.

*T*he Weldon is hard to beat when it is time to combine comfort, convenience and a narrow lot. The covered porch is the perfect bridge between the outdoor barbecue and the sliding doors that lead to the kitchenette. Take another step and your guests will enjoy a private area that includes their own closet, shower, a place to change and their own bathroom facility. And be sure to note the double doors that guarantee full use of the out-of-the-way storage area.

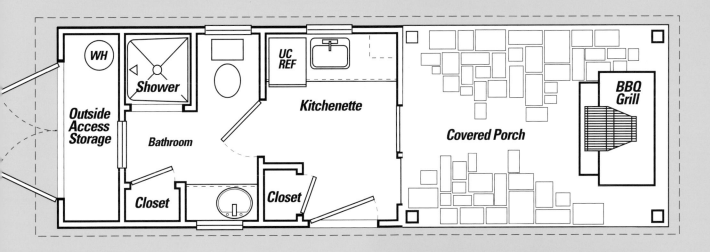

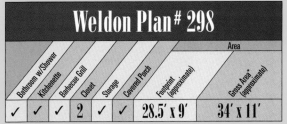

Weldon Plan # 298

Bathroom w/Shower	Kitchenette	Barbecue Grill	Closet	Storage	Covered Porch	Footprint (approximate)	Gross Area* (approximate)
✓	✓	✓	2	✓	✓	28.5' x 9'	34' x 11'

*Suggested minimum area to build this plan to accommodate door openings, roof overhangs, exterior walls, treatments and easy access.

Williston

he family that has the Williston on its property has a look that is truly distinctive. The seamed metal roof, double arches and decorative fan moldings over the French doors combine to make this an appealing design. But the Williston is more than just another pretty face. It is easy to picture yourself having a refreshing outdoor shower and then relaxing in the shaded comfort of the over-sized porch.

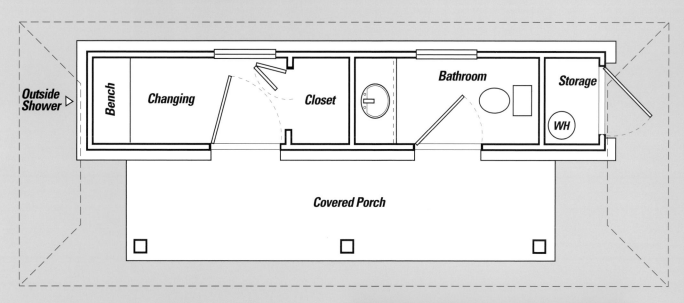

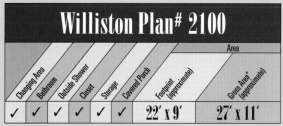

Williston Plan# 2100

							Area	
Changing Area	Bathroom	Outside Shower	Closet	Storage	Covered Porch	Footprint (approximate)	Gross Area* (approximate)	
✓	✓	✓	✓	✓	✓	22' x 9'	27' x 11'	

*Suggested minimum area to build this plan to accommodate door openings, roof overhangs, exterior walls, treatments and easy access.

Windham

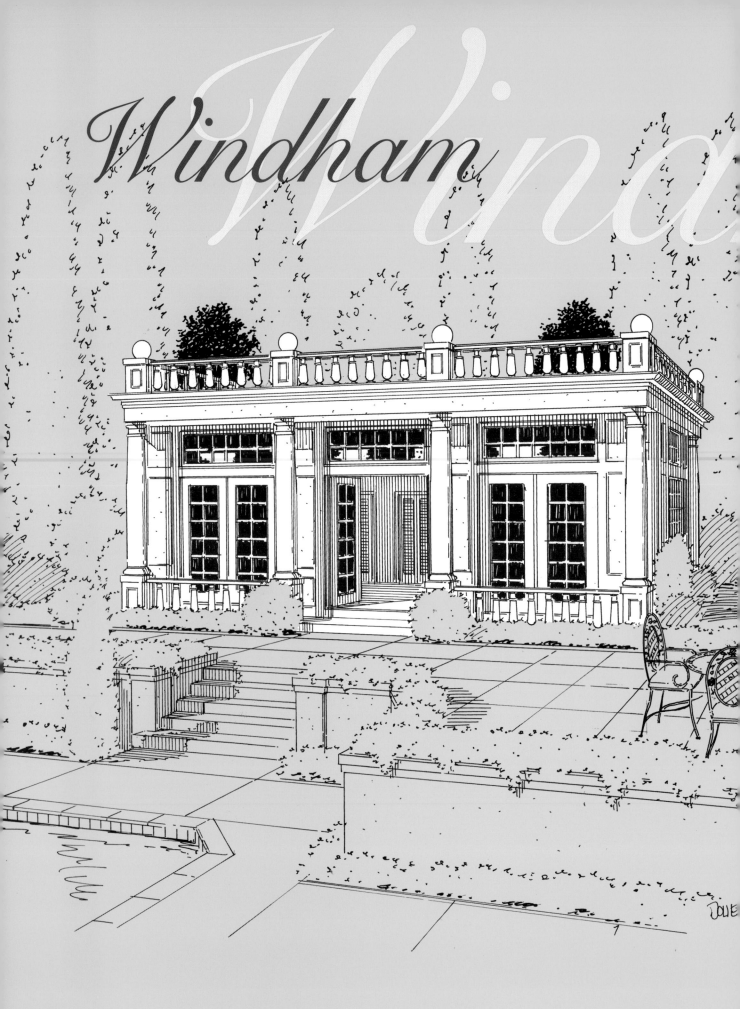

*T*his is the pièce de résistance *in outdoor entertainment. It boasts two large bathrooms, each with an adjoining shower. The grand entertainment area is tiled and surrounded on three sides by walls of glass, including the glass double doors at the entrance. The Windham, a true showpiece, is executed in the Beaux Arts style. You will be able to use the convenient kitchenette for your guests—but you will have to hire your own string quartet.*

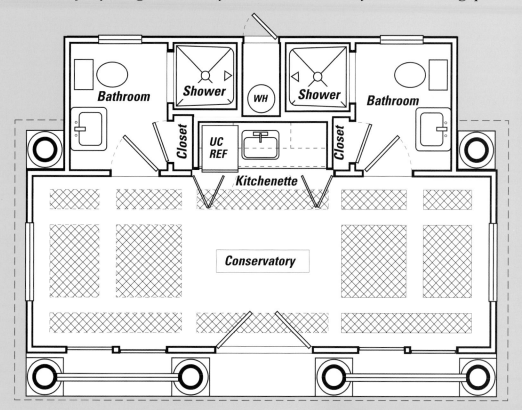

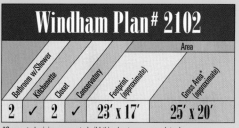

Windham Plan # 2102

Bathroom w/Shower	Kitchenette	Closet	Conservatory	Footprint (approximate)	Area Gross Area* (approximate)
2	✓	2	✓	23' x 17'	25' x 20'

*Suggested minimum area to build this plan to accommodate door openings, roof overhangs, exterior walls, treatments and easy access.

Winthrop

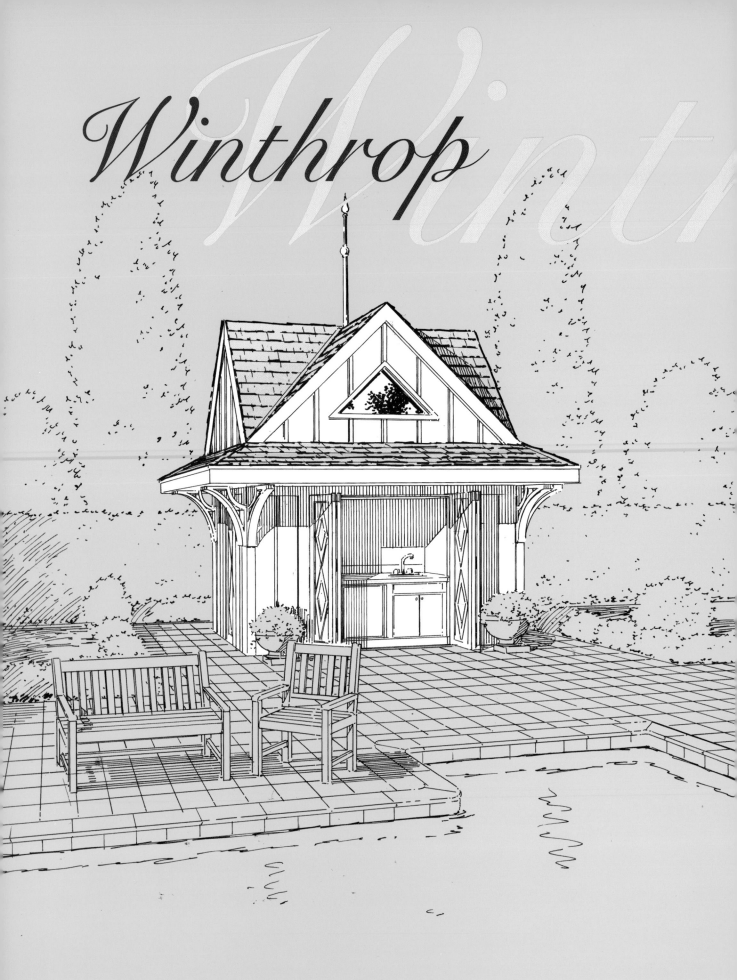

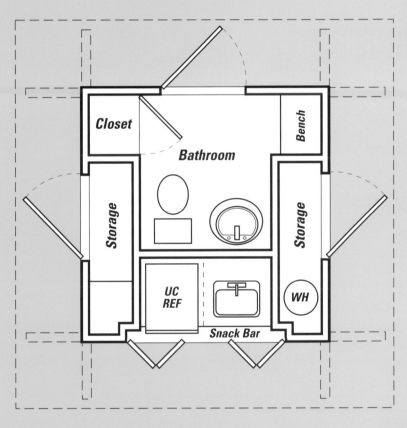

Closet

Bathroom

Bench

Storage

Storage

UC REF

WH

Snack Bar

*T*his Victorian makes the point that even those who have very little extra ground can still have a pool house with just about everything. The snack bar is so handy that you can get an afternoon treat and be back in the pool before a drop of water hits the ground. The changing room/bathroom is in the back, and each side has an outdoor storage area for added convenience.

Winthrop Plan # 2104

| | | | | Area | |
Bathroom	Snack Bar	Closet	Storage	Footprint (approximate)	Gross Area* (approximate)
✓	✓	✓	2	8' x 8'	16' x 16'

*Suggested minimum area to build this plan to accommodate door openings, roof overhangs, exterior walls, treatments and easy access.

Compact ❖ Design

Brewster

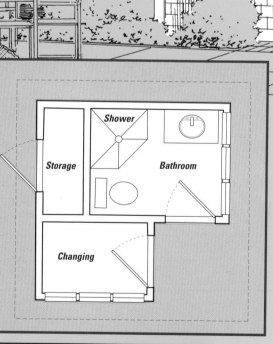

If you believe that the subject of "sighs" counts more than "size," the Brewster is for you. Even though this pool house does not take up a lot of space, there is room for a bathroom with a shower, a changing room and storage for pool accessories. The Brewster is perfect for pool owners who know that limited space does not have to result in limited family convenience.

Brewster Plan# 3106

Bathroom w/Shower	Changing Area	Storage	Footprint (approximate)	Gross Area* (approximate)
✓	✓	✓	10' x 10'	14' x 13'

*Suggested minimum area to build this plan to accommodate door openings, roof overhangs, exterior walls, treatments and easy access.

Compact ◆ Design

Harrison

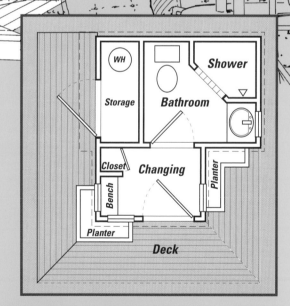

*W*hoever said, "Good things come in small packages" must have had the Harrison in mind. In addition to the changing room, the plans include space for an out-of-the-way storage area for pool chemicals and for a bathroom with a corner shower. Notice the attractive planters and decking, and you will see why the Harrison is a wonderful choice for those who want a family pool house without cashing in the family jewels.

Harrison Plan# 3107

Bathroom w/Shower	Changing Area	Closet	Storage	Planter	Deck	Footprint (approximate)	Gross Area (approximate)
✓	✓	✓	✓	2	✓	9' x 10'	13' x 14'

*Suggested minimum area to build this plan to accommodate door openings, roof overhangs, exterior walls, treatments and easy access.

Compact ❖ Design

Lakeside

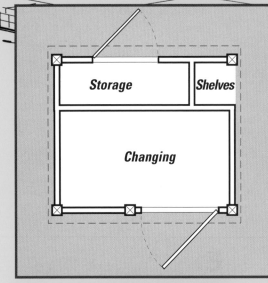

	Storage	
		Shelves
Changing		

Lakeside Plan # 3108

Changing Area	Storage	Outdoor Shelving	Footprint (approximate)	Area Gross Area* (approximate)
✓	✓	✓	6' x 5'	8' x 11'

*Suggested minimum area to build this plan to accommodate door openings, roof overhangs, exterior walls, treatments and easy access.

Coventry has great choices for pool houses when space is at a premium, and the Lakeside is a fine example. It has a changing room, outdoor shelving and a small storage closet in back. Lakeside makes the point that there is plenty of room for design and creativity, regardless of size.

Compact ◆ Design

Monroe

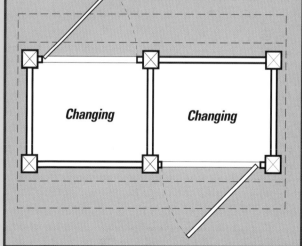

*W*hen it comes to economy, the Monroe takes the prize. That is true for its size, its simple design, its openness, and even for its budget-minded corrugated plastic roof. If you are a do-it-yourselfer, take note: the Monroe will last for umpteen years, but can probably be built for less money than your family spent on last year's vacation.

Changing   Changing

Monroe Plan # 3109

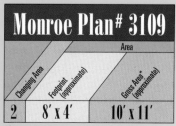

		Area	
Changing Area	Footprint (approximate)		Gross Area* (approximate)
2	8' x 4'		10' x 11'

*Suggested minimum area to build this plan to accommodate door openings, roof overhangs, exterior walls, treatments and easy access.

Compact ❖ Design

Stanton

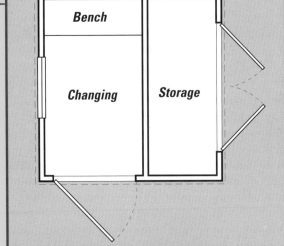

Here is a recipe for success: take a pool area where the space is limited and add basic functionality, an interesting roof design, a pinch of cedar shakes and a helping of horizontal siding. Voilà! A design that makes the point that everyone who has a pool has room for some type of pool house.

Stanton Plan # 3110

Changing Area	Storage	Footprint (approximate)	Area Gross Area* (approximate)
✓	✓	6' x 6'	9' x 10'

*Suggested minimum area to build this plan to accommodate door openings, roof overhangs, exterior walls, treatments and easy access.

Garden Houses

A peaceful getaway or the perfect workstation: a garden house can be whatever you want it to be. Some people enjoy the idea of being able to escape to a secret place. Others prefer a functional place for storing their garden tools and for potting or harvesting the results of their hard labor. Still others desire a place that is an artistic expression of their favorite dream. The garden houses

featured on the following pages are all of those and more. You can modify them to meet the style of your main house, or you can use them as pool houses or storage spaces. Whichever house you decide to build will undoubtedly become your favorite place to escape to...to work in...to dream in....

Contempra

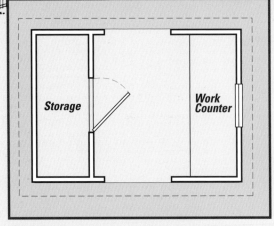

Contempra Plan# 4112

Work Counter	Storage	Footprint (approximate)	Gross Area* (approximate)
		Area	
✓	✓	12' x 8'	14' x 10'

*Suggested minimum area to build this plan to accommodate door openings, roof overhangs, exterior walls, treatments and easy access.

*L*ike a cool breeze on a hot summer day, the Contempra will refresh every garden it adorns. The enchanting pass-through design gives access to a storage closet for tools and other garden accessories, plus, there is a generous amount of counter space that is easy to get to when your hands are full. The best thing about this house is that even though it takes up so little room in your garden, it is so impressive to the eye.

Daydream

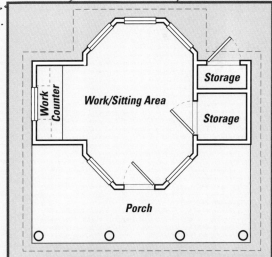

Here you will find an incredible floor plan to go along with spectacular elevations all around this spacious garden house. The front porch is homey and big enough for a rocker or two. Inside, there is plenty of storage and counter space. There is also a large functional room that is perfect for entertaining or for working on special projects. Yes, this garden house has more quality features than any daydream has a right to have.

Daydream Plan # 4113

Work Counter	Work Area	Storage	Porch	Footprint (approximate)	Gross Area* (approximate)
				Area	
✓	✓	2	✓	17.4' x 17.4'	20' x 21'

*Suggested minimum area to build this plan to accommodate door openings, roof overhangs, exterior walls, treatments and easy access.

Delphinium

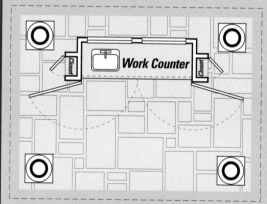

Closet | Work Counter | Closet

Delphinium Plan # 4114

			Area	
Work Counter	Closet	Footprint (approximate)		Gross Area* (approximate)
✓	2	14.6' x 10.6'		17' x 13'

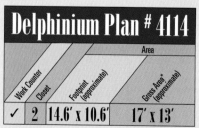

*Suggested minimum area to build this plan to accommodate door openings, roof overhangs, exterior walls, treatments and easy access.

*N*othing stands as straight as this favored "flower" of the garden. This is a place for tea with guests or solitude with nature; a space of brilliant light, colorful stone paving, hidden workspace and the wondrous open-air theater all around. It is the destination of your imagination and awaits you as a royal garden treasure.

Great Escape

This is the special place you have had in mind. It has all of the amenities to make it the destination of choice of discriminating gardeners worldwide. A magnificent airy porch leads to a multi-functional internal space that is more than just practical. With the right amount of storage, both inside and out, the Great Escape can easily happen before your eyes.

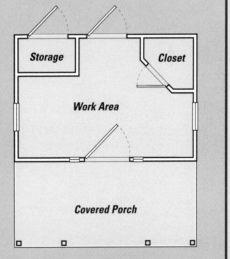

Storage

Closet

Work Area

Covered Porch

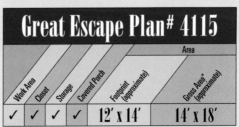

Great Escape Plan # 4115

				Area	
Work Area	Closet	Storage	Covered Porch	Footprint (approximate)	Gross Area* (approximate)
✓	✓	✓	✓	12' x 14'	14' x 18'

*Suggested minimum area to build this plan to accommodate door openings, roof overhangs, exterior walls, treatments and easy access.

Rosebud

Storage

Work Counter

Work Area

Rosebud Plan# 4116

			Area	
Work Counter	Work Area	Storage	Footprint (approximate)	Gross Area* (approximate)
✓	✓	✓	12.6' x 12.6'	16' x 16'

*Suggested minimum area to build this plan to accommodate door openings, roof overhangs, exterior walls, treatments and easy access.

*N*ot a line from a famous movie, but a brilliant flower in the making. So beautifully proportioned, its functionality takes a back seat to its captivating grace. The Rosebud features plenty of storage and counter space, plus a wonderful room for any type of work you can conjure up. This star of the garden can easily be converted to a pool house.

Shato

*I*nspired by a Japanese temple, this beautiful edifice will become the ultimate centerpiece in any garden. Using indigenous trees, tree trunks, timbers and stones, the Shato will blend with nature, yet have a stunning impact on your property. Its decorative ridgeline towers over a small footprint to create a larger than life image that will beckon visitors as well as captivate the spirit of "one-of-a-kind" gardeners.

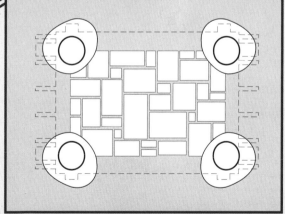

Shato Plan# 4117

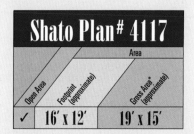

Open Area	Area	
	Footprint (approximate)	Gross Area* (approximate)
✓	16' x 12'	19' x 15'

*Suggested minimum area to build this plan to accommodate door openings, roof overhangs, exterior walls, treatments and easy access.

Summer Cottage

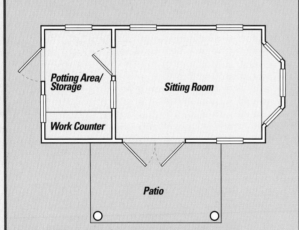

Potting Area/Storage

Sitting Room

Work Counter

Patio

Summer Cottage Plan # 4118

Sitting Room	Work Counter	Potting Area/Storage	Patio	Footprint (approximate)	Area	
					Gross Area* (approximate)	
✓	✓	✓	✓	17.6' x 16'	23' x 18'	

*Suggested minimum area to build this plan to accommodate door openings, roof overhangs, exterior walls, treatments and easy access.

*R*eminiscent of a small cottage by a stream or deep in your dreams, this place can be reserved for afternoon tea with biscuits, or as a weekend retreat from all the things you really need to do. The sitting room is large enough for any passing thought, and the storage room is of generous proportions. Outside, every view adds to the charm and the lure of your summer place.

Victoria

Picture yourself: it is mid-afternoon, and you have just finished planting a perennial border. You have put away your tools and are waiting for the water in the electric teapot to boil. All around you the large windows of your garden house reveal nature at its finest. It is a picture of splendid color and tranquility. Your favorite book is resting on the glass table-top, and the matching wrought-iron chair awaits you. You could not be happier. The Victoria garden house is exactly what the doctor ordered.

Work Counter

Work Counter

Victoria Plan# 4119

			Area	
Work Area	Work Counter	Footprint (approximate)	Gross Area* (approximate)	
✓	✓	13' x 8'	15' x 10'	

*Suggested minimum area to build this plan to accommodate door openings, roof overhangs, exterior walls, treatments and easy access.

Summer Houses

*W*here do you go when you just want to while away the time, read a book by your favorite author, enjoy a cup of tea or just relax? Traditionally, the English have retreated to the sanctuary of their gardens and summerhouses. In the past, some of England's most famous literary figures disappeared into their summerhouses to escape the noise and distractions of everyday life. Henry James, Sir Walter Scott and Charles Dickens used them as backdrops for pivotal scenes in their works. Today, the summerhouse remains a necessity for many of the English.

However, its use has changed. No longer just a safe haven from life's pressures, it now serves as an office, a studio, even as an extra room. On the following pages, five of Amdega's summerhouses are featured. Just imagine one gracing your landscape, offering you a place to withdraw to when you need solitude. If you require additional information, contact Amdega LTD directly at 1-800-449-7348.

The Belvedere Gazebo

*T*he word gazebo derives from the eighteenth century, when some learned and humorous mind added the Latin suffix that means "I shall" to the English word "gaze," hence "I shall look out." The gazebo is more open and airy than a summerhouse, and the Belvedere features distinctive ogee arches on its open sides. The Belvedere is available in two sizes: 10' octagonal, or 7' hexagonal.

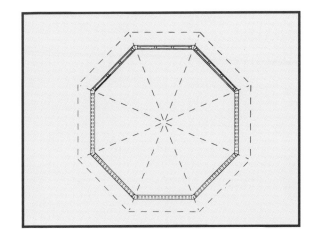

The Gaywood

One of the biggest models in the Amdega LTD summerhouse range, the Gaywood follows in the tradition of the garden pavilions of old. Its rectangular shape and large dimensions create a number of possible uses, both practical and pleasurable, from home office to mini pavilion and somewhere to sit back and watch a game of tennis or croquet. This model is available in two sizes: 12′ x 8′ or 10′ x 7′.

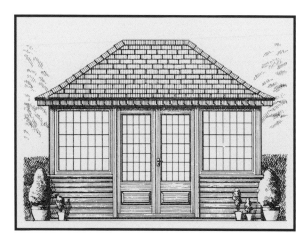

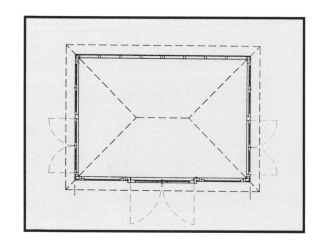

Order directly from Amdega LTD: 1-800-449-7348

The *Jubilee*

*S*pace and comfort are vital, particularly when creating a relaxing hideaway from the main house. Octagonal in shape and generous in size, the Jubilee makes a splendid garden room and the perfect setting to enjoy a lazy summer lunch party, afternoon tea, or a dinner party on a balmy night. Available in two sizes, 10′ x 10′ or 12′ (10 sides), the Jubilee would also make a peaceful studio, music room or fishing hut.

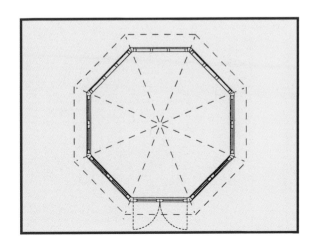

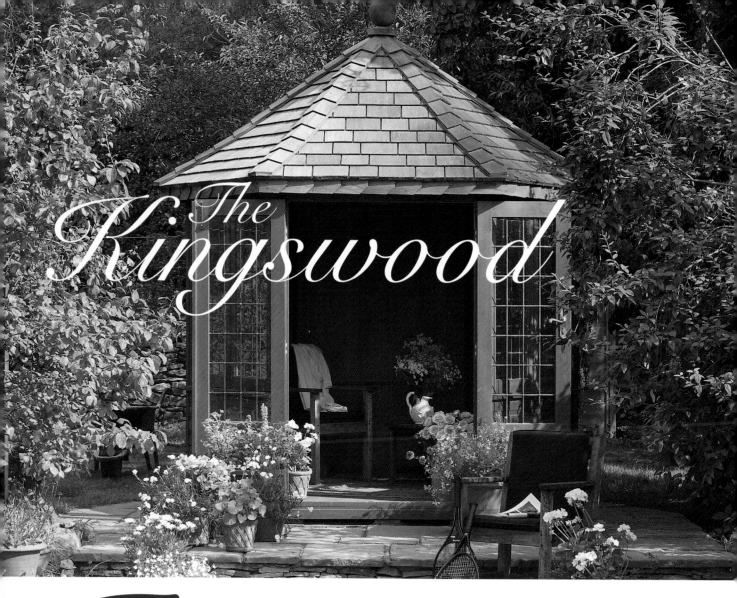

The Kingswood

*T*his six sided, pretty little summerhouse is a versatile and practical extension to gardens of any size, shape or location. For the smaller townhouse, perhaps with a rectangular garden, the Kingswood is an attractive addition to the urban setting: a natural flavor of the country in town. Alternatively, its good looks and neat dimensions would easily blend into a suburban, or large country house garden. Size 7′ x 7′.

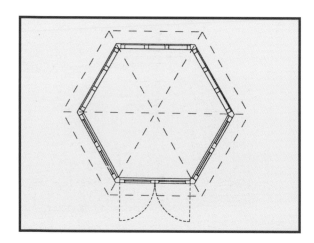

The *Wraylands*

With handcrafted leaded light on all but one of its four timber walls and generous double doors, the Wraylands can be placed almost anywhere in the garden, creating a bright and tranquil haven throughout the day. This neat little square house would suit a small townhouse garden, as much as it would the sprawling lawns of a large country house. Size 8' x 8'.

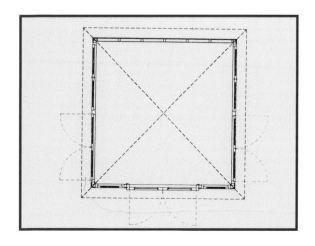

Important Order Information

Speed of Delivery

We prepare your order the day it is received. However, since each set of plans is custom-made, please allow 2 to 3 days for processing. For more information about ordering plans, call 1-800-887-2011.

Customizing

Your professional builder can assist you in making minor changes or material substitutions. For other changes, consult a professional architect or design service.

Mechanical Details

Heating, plumbing and air-conditioning details vary on the basis of climate, local codes, type of system used and type of energy used. Specifications and plans should be obtained from your local contractor, builder or supplier.

Codes and Seals

All of our plans are designed to meet or exceed national building standards. States and municipalities have their own codes and building requirements, including permit and inspection ordinances. It is important that you consult with a local professional, making plan modifications as needed, to comply with these requirements.

Some locations require that an architect or engineer "seal" building plans before construction begins. This seal can normally be obtained for a nominal fee from your local government.

Refunds and Exchanges

Each set of plans is printed and shipped to you after we receive your order. Therefore, we cannot honor requests for refunds or exchanges.

Summerhouses

Contact Amdega LTD concerning the summerhouses. For information about construction and prices, call 1-800-449-7348, or write to 16 Ostend Avenue, Westport, CT 06880.

Pricing Code

Pool Houses

Alegría	B
Ashton	C
Barrington	C
Breezewood	C
Bromley	C
Captain's Paradise	D
Captain's Retreat	D
Carlisle	D
Chandler	C
Concord	B
Cumberland	D
Cypress	C
Dorchester	B
El Sol	C
Emerson	C
Fairview	C
Glenville	C
Hacienda	D
Hamilton	B
Hancock	C

Kenwood	C
La Bonita	D
Laguna	C
Lansford	B
Marquesa	D
Milford	C
Montegra	D
Montpelier	B
Newfield	C
Pendleton	B
Pennington	C
Piedmont	B
Rockford	D
St. Marie	C
Seaside	C
Shelby	C
Springdale	D
Sundance	D
The Tower	D
Townsend	B
Valencia	C

Weldon	D
Williston	B
Windham	D
Winthrop	B

Compact Designs

Brewster	B
Harrison	B
Lakeside	A
Monroe	A
Stanton	A

Garden Houses

Contempra	A
Daydream	D
Delphinium	C
Great Escape	B
Rosebud	B
Shato	B
Summer Cottage	C
Victoria	C

How to Order Plans

Each Set of Plans Includes:
1. Foundation plan
2. Floor plan complete with electrical layout and plumbing fixtures indicated
3. All exterior elevations (front, rear and sides)
4. Roof details
5. Cabinet and vanity locations and details
6. Any necessary wall sections and details

Notes
1. All plans must be ordered at the same time to receive the multiple set pricing. Any orders for additional sets will be treated as new orders and will be priced accordingly.
2. All orders are final. Plans may not be returned or exchanged.
3. No C.O.D orders
4. Send no cash.

Price of Plans
Prices effective July 1, 2003

Pricing Code

Number of Sets	A	B	C	D
One	$95	$190	$280	$360
Two	$105	$210	$300	$380
Three	$115	$230	$320	$400
Four	$125	$250	$340	$420
Five	$135	$260	$350	$430

Over five: add $15 per set

Prices are subject to change without notice. Please call for information.

FAX Orders
(credit cards only)
215-364-6847

To order summerhouses, call 1-800-449-7348 or write to: Amdega/Machin, 16 Ostend Avenue, Westport, CT 06880

Phone Orders
(credit cards only)
1-800-887-2011
Between the hours of 9 A.M. and 5 P.M., Eastern Time

Mail Order Form
Money Order, Check or Credit Card.
Make checks and money orders payable to:
MANOR HOUSE PUBLISHING CO., INC.

Name and # of Model	Number of Sets	Price Code	Total
			$
			$
			$
			$

Shipping
Shipping and Handling Fee: $9.95 $ _____
(We ship UPS Ground; call 1-800-887-2011 for other shipping methods and prices)

Sales Tax: PA residents add 6% $ _____

Total Enclosed $ _____

Shipping Information
(No PO Box numbers; must include street address)

Name _____

Address _____

City _____

State _____

Zip _____

Telephone Number (   ) _____

Credit Card Orders: ☐ Visa   ☐ MasterCard

Name on Card _____

Card Number _____

Expiration Date _____

Signature _____
(required)

Mail to: MANOR HOUSE PUBLISHING CO., INC.
860 Pennsylvania Blvd., Feasterville, PA 19053
Visit our Web site: www.poolhouses.com

127